Coffee Talk

Published by Mater Media
St. Louis, Missouri
www.matermedia.org

Editor: Kari Sherman
Cover and Interior Design: Trese Gloriod

Printed in the USA.

978-1-7365190-5-9

Coffee Talk

A Transformational Tale Inspired by the Imitation of Christ

Bryan Taylor and Michael Kroth

MATER
MEDIA

Chapter 1

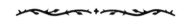

The sudden development of a late summer thunderstorm brought welcome relief to the town of Kempis, Idaho. After a dry August, the thriving college town was badly in need of a drink, and the dark gray clouds rolling in were happy to oblige. As the blackening sky opened, torrents of water quickly soaked the sidewalks, forcing surprised pedestrians to search for cover.

Grayson Rogers, PhD, instantly regretted his decision to walk to his favorite coffee shop as wisps of steam rose from the hot cement and swirled around his shoes. Although the sudden shower matted his silver hair and permeated his tweed jacket, the water's intrusion on his body was an inconsequential prelude to what was coming next.

Just two blocks ahead he could see the familiar red brick building and was focusing all his efforts on getting there quickly. Suddenly a flash of light exploded, landing too close for comfort. Grayson was momentarily blinded, as a loud clap rang in his ears. He could feel the heat and the air crackled. If there was a meter that measured the sound of thunder, this would have certainly moved the needle to the top. Shaking involuntarily, Grayson struggled to regain his hearing as well as his composure.

For some time, he had amused himself by dreaming up endings to an autobiography he had yet to begin. This near-miss nature strike bolted him with the realization that the unwritten book had come uncomfortably close to a devastating last chapter.

After several deep breaths, he instinctively quickened his pace toward the familiar painted sign that read "Cozy Roaster" in elegant script. As he pulled open the door, he was greeted by the familiar aroma of freshly brewed coffee and old books. After his near-death experience, he quickly scanned the crowd for a comforting face until his gaze landed on his favorite former student, who was now his favorite barista.

Lucy Finley spotted her mentor and let out a gasp. His wet dog appearance caught her off guard, but it was the fear in his eyes that was even more out of place. She quickly wiped her crumb-covered hands on the golden yellow words sprawled across her black apron.

"Dr. G are you alright?" she exclaimed worriedly as she motioned Grayson toward the counter.

He let out an audible sigh as his heart rate slowed. Lucy's reassuring voice confirmed that the ringing had ceased, and his hearing had returned to normal. He walked deeper into the well-known establishment as his wet shoes squeaked across the lightly creaking floor.

"Lucy, I just almost got hit by lightning." After a short pause and debating whether to laugh or cry, he let out a nervous chuckle.

The laughter gave Lucy hope that the strike had not been as close as he was making it sound, but the glassy look in his eyes wouldn't lie.

Grayson shook his head and sighed, "You know, lightning or no lightning, it's been another sucky day."

Lucy swallowed hard as her mind rolled back to freshman year when this same professor had imparted the pithy advice, "Don't LET your day be sucky." So much had changed since then.

"Oh, Dr. G, I wish I was off so we could talk."

Like most of his former students, Lucy referred to Grayson by the first letter of his first name instead of his last. He considered it an affectionate gesture and a testament to his unintimidating persona.

"I'll go brew up your usual. Why don't you dry off and have a seat? I'll bring it over as soon as it's done." Lucy passed him a clean bar towel from the drawer behind the counter and hurried off to make his vanilla double espresso, a concoction that was both energizing and comforting, much like Dr. G's former demeanor. It was interesting that his coffee preference seemed to cling to who he used to be.

Grayson had been frequenting the Cozy Roaster ever since he started teaching in Kempis. It opened the same year he arrived and was situated just south of campus. Sure, there was a Starbucks just two blocks away from his office, but that was a formulaic franchise. Some students preferred Java Joint, the trendy new coffee shop in town, equipped with track lighting, shiny granite, and modern art displayed on the walls. But like a stray dog who lingers close to the hand that feeds it, Grayson was faithfully drawn to the warm, yellow lights and feeling of this second home. They had been through life together, and like his heart, the 2-inch thick rustic countertops held many scars. The reclaimed oak had served drinks, absorbed spills, and boasted scratches from the thousands of scholars who had filtered in from the nearby dorms through the years. In all its imperfections, it was sturdy and dependable, two qualities that Grayson desperately needed in his life, especially after the past year.

Unlike the coordinated, contemporary furniture at the Java Joint, the Cozy Roaster featured a mishmash of tables and chairs of various shapes and sizes, each as unique as the patrons who entered the doors. Numerous pieces were older than the students who sat in them. Grayson loved that the décor in here never changed with the trends; this place was the one aspect of his life that he could always count on staying the same.

"Dr. G, did you forget your umbrella?" a student at a nearby table commented as the soaking wet professor passed by on his way to the restroom.

"No, I just decided not to use it." Grayson joked sarcastically, trying to hide the shakiness still lingering in his voice. Some teachers become crotchety after years in education, but honing his come-back skills kept Grayson genial.

Grayson made his way down the hallway and grabbed the long sturdy handle on a door that read "Gents" and stepped inside the slightly brighter space. The men's room at the Cozy Roaster was just as charming and unchanged over the years as the rest of the place. Grayson's brown loafers clicked as they hit the black and white checkered tile. When he gazed in the mirror, his reflection caught him off guard. The man staring back at him had the complexion of a ghost with silvery hair sprawled out in all directions. Trying to freshen up, Grayson splashed cold water on his cheeks and patted them a few times, slapping the trauma out of his expression.

He used the towel Lucy had given him to dry off as best he

could. The removal of his tweed jacket, which had received the brunt of the rain's beating, revealed a navy and white plaid buttoned shirt. It had been his wife's favorite because it brought out a slight hint of blue in his hazel eyes. Grayson wondered what she would say if she could see him now.

This never would have happened if Piper were still here. She would have checked the weather and told me to take my car.

He finished by using his fingers to comb his mangled hair to the side, hoping the dampness would hold it in place.

A final glance in the mirror confirmed he was ready to go sip his hot coffee and calm his nerves completely in *his* chair. There was something about the cozy chair in the far corner by itself that always made the hard days better.

The bulk of the furniture in the Cozy Roaster was arranged for groups. But over by the gray stone fireplace, was an oversized, chestnut brown, high back leather chair. It was well-worn, and over the years had learned to conform to Grayson's body like a warm hug. It was known by the regulars as "the Dr. G chair," although no one had ever formally christened it as such. Respect for the professor was so great that when he entered the establishment, any student occupying it would immediately find somewhere else to sit. If Grayson felt like socializing, he would help himself to a folding chair from the nearby supply closet and place it across from the rickety table that sat in front of the Dr. G chair. Much to the dismay of the students who loved him, the closet mostly stayed closed these days.

As Grayson exited the restroom and headed toward the counter to return the towel, he couldn't help but notice all the students on their phones and laptops. He scoffed silently as he thought back to a time before cell phones when the world seemed easier. He never said it aloud, but he abhorred the idea that online learning was the future. Yes, it was economically advantageous for institutions and often increased efficiency, but in his heart, he knew that in-person learning was where the magic happens. Students engaging in spontaneous, lively discussions with their professors bore the type of fruit that could never be replaced by machines. Face-to-face instruction also helped to foster personal connections with students, like the special mentor relationship he had built with Lucy Finley.

Although he was a revered, tenured philosophy professor who still had his health, a wealth of knowledge, and a love for helping students succeed, the new direction of college education was a gut punch that pushed him right into deciding to retire after 35 years. His desire to leave was compounded by the changes in his personal life, and this coffee shop snapshot was a quick reminder that he had made the right choice to walk away.

On his way back over to Lucy, Grayson decided to make a quick stop to set his briefcase and wet coat next to his chair. As he headed in that direction, he noticed something that turned his bad mood even more sour. *Of all the days for this to happen, of course it had to be this one.*

There in some sort of academic glory was a professional-looking stranger sitting in *his* chair like he owned the place. His slightly overgrown, sideswept blonde hair was glistening in the soft lighting, and his foot, sporting a gray Oxford, swung slowly back and forth on top of his crossed legs. He was clearly immersed in a book and comfortable. A little too comfortable. The man looked older than a freshman, so Grayson was slightly irritated that he didn't notice him and quickly move like all the others.

This type of thing would happen occasionally when someone new came into the coffee shop. Typically, a nearby student would come to his rescue and notify the newbie of the unspoken rules, but today, all the students were buried in their screens and didn't notice the distressing scene.

I never used to get bothered by this type of thing. What's happened to me?

He decided again to switch directions and head back to the counter. The face of his favorite barista and former teaching assistant always brought him comfort.

Over the past year, Lucy had noticed a subtle shift in the demeanor of her friend and mentor. Today he seemed more "off" than normal and that concerned her.

As he walked over, she managed to hide her worry. "Dr. G, I just finished your drink. I was about to bring it over."

Grayson was more concerned about the stranger in his chair than getting his caffeine fix.

"Lucy, do you have any idea who that guy might be?" he groaned as he discreetly pointed toward his corner.

Lucy's head swiveled to take the stranger in. Her long, wavy auburn hair, tied back in a low ponytail, shifted behind her Cozy Roaster t-shirt as she looked around. The chair's occupant did not look like a student, nor did he dress like one. Instead of an old hoodie and sweats, he wore a blue blazer over neatly pressed jeans.

"Sorry Dr. G, I've never seen him before. I didn't even notice him come in." Lucy could tell her mentor was perturbed. She wondered to herself why this man would plant himself in the coffee shop without ordering anything, but a new customer walked in, forcing her to divert her attention.

"Welcome to the Cozy Roaster. What can I get for you?" she greeted the student with her warm smile.

Grayson sighed and scanned the room. The semester had started last week, and the summer slump was officially over. Every table was full of students, and none of them looked like they were close to leaving. He thought about asking Lucy to put his coffee in a to-go cup, but a quick glance toward the rain outside made him shudder and convinced him it was best to wait for the storm to completely pass over.

Grayson tucked his briefcase underneath his arm and grabbed his espresso. The hot ceramic seared his fingertips, but he ignored the pain. He'd become good at that lately.

When he noticed that the only empty space in the room was across from the neatly dressed stranger, he had no choice but to set up camp there. He used his free hand to set the chair from the supply closet down with a loud clunk, purposefully making it slightly louder than it needed to be. He was half hoping the stranger would notice him and move, but to his dismay, the man was engrossed in his book and never looked up.

Grayson, an avid reader himself, glanced at the cover, wondering what work a young professional might be so captivated by. The book had a well-worn leather cover, but it was hard for his aging eyes to make out the words. He squinted and leaned in a little closer, trying to make out the gilded letters embossed on the cover. After leaning in a little more, he saw *De Imitatione Christi*. His Latin had gotten rusty over the years, but he recognized the title.

A deep pain hit his chest as he remembered why the title sounded familiar. His mind flashed years back to an anniversary dinner at Sherman's Steakhouse. He could almost feel the linen napkin in his lap and taste the filet mignon, as he remembered Piper handing him a small, wrapped present across the table. The green book she gifted him had the same title as the book in the man's hands. At the time it had been a cherished gift, but he had never made the time to read it. Now a tinge of guilt struck him.

He snapped out of his brief déjà vu moment when the young man suddenly lowered the book and seemed startled by his gaze. Grayson hadn't noticed how far he had been encroaching on the man's personal space. As the stranger's green eyes met his, Grayson stuttered, slightly embarrassed, "Oh, pardon me, I was just staring at your book. I'm curious to know if the entire content is in Latin."

The man chuckled, relieved that it was just an old man with bad eyes and not something worse sneaking up on him. "Oh, no. Just the cover." He held the book up in his muscular right hand and smiled. "Are you familiar with it?"

"Yes...Well, no." Grayson stammered. "I recognized the title."

The sting came back as he thought once again about his late wife. The wound was still as fresh as if it had happened yesterday.

The stranger marked his place with the gold ribbon bound into the spine and set the book on the table in between them.

9

"It's a fascinating read. I highly recommend it."

Mentally filing the unsolicited suggestion, Grayson cleared his throat and extended his hand. "I'm Grayson Rogers."

Pensive and pausing a moment to take the elderly professor in, the stranger's eyes widened in a starstruck gaze. "Wait a minute—*Doctor* Grayson Rogers?"

Grayson raised an eyebrow apprehensively, scanning his memory. "Have we met?"

"No, but I feel like I know you! I read a couple of your books while doing research for my dissertation. I really admired the way you delivered such complicated ideas with great clarity. Your writing is thought provoking and just brilliant!"

The compliment loosened Grayson up a bit, and for a moment he decided not to hold it against the man that he was still sitting in *his* chair. He smiled shyly and joked, "I'm glad *someone* got something out of those books."

The truth was tens of thousands had "gotten something" out of the twelve books he had authored.

The stranger sat up straighter and adjusted his jacket. "I'm honored to meet you sir. I hardly recognized you from that one headshot they seem to use in all your books."

Grayson laughed. "The publisher loved that photo and insisted we keep using it." *Man, that was 20 years ago, and I bet I look 30 years older now.*

"My name is Matthew Arcanum. I just got my doctorate last year and was hired to teach theology at the university," he said casually, pointing his thumb toward the iconic clock tower on campus.

Arcanum. Sounds familiar. Grayson racked his brain and was again reminded of his rusty Latin. He had instruction in the language during his Catholic school days, but that seemed like another lifetime ago. That was back when he was sure there was a God. Now, he was convinced that one could never really know.

"Ah. Theology, the study of God. Well, welcome to Kempis!"

Matthew sensed something deeper behind Grayson's words, but he didn't want to pry.

"Thank you, Professor. How long have you and your wife lived here?"

There was that sting again. Grayson swallowed the rising lump in his throat. It had been exactly 298 days since Piper had made him a widower. "We moved here 35 years ago, but my wife passed last year," Grayson solemnly replied.

Matthew could hear the pain in his voice and instantly regretted asking the question.

Grayson quickly tried to change the subject. "What about you Matthew? Certainly, a handsome young man like yourself has found a sweet little lady to settle down with. Are you married?"

Grayson got the impression he had returned an awkward question when Matthew quickly placed his right hand over his ring finger. Grayson caught a quick glimpse of silver as the young man replied, "I am."

Matthew seemed to be searching desperately to change the subject, but after a glance at his watch he announced "I've got to run. Nice to meet you, Dr. Rogers."

Matthew threw his camel-colored leather satchel over his shoulder, stuffed *De Imitatione Christi* carefully inside the front flap, and beelined for the exit.

"Please, call me Grayson," he called while Matthew scurried out the door.

I doubt he even heard me. I wonder why he was in such a hurry.

He meandered around the table and slumped abruptly into his now vacant chair. He couldn't put his finger on it, but there was something quite different about this new professor.

Chapter 2

Grayson noticed his Timex hit 2:00, triggering him to take a hesitant glance out the large front window. The sun's rays were piercing through the dissipating gray, and according to the weather app on his phone, the storm was long gone. After the events of that morning, he would have preferred completely clear skies to walk home with, but he knew Stoli, his beloved corgi, would need to go out soon. He quickly gulped down the rest of his coffee, said goodbye to Lucy, and headed toward home.

Grayson lived in a modest, burgundy, all-brick ranch-style home built in the seventies. Decades ago, when they had been searching for a home, Piper insisted on this one because it was only half a mile from campus. As he approached his street, he couldn't help but think about how Piper had hoped a short commute would mean more time spent together. Now, he wondered if he had made that their reality. The shorter distance to campus had meant easy access to work, and he always thought they'd have their golden years together. If he had known they wouldn't, he would have done some things differently.

As he walked up the stone path to his white front door, he could see Stoli in the bay window wagging his tail excitedly. The 15-year-old corgi was one of the only things these days that could bring an unforced smile to Grayson's face. As they were unable to have children, Stoli had brought much needed joy and amusement into Piper and Grayson's lives. They had rescued him when he was just a puppy, and he had become like a beloved son to them.

When Grayson opened the door, Stoli hopped down onto his too-short-for-his-body legs and waddled over to meet him. Even though he didn't have the vigor and agility he used to, he could still muster up enough energy to get to and from his favorite spot in the world. The bay window was Stoli's Cozy Roaster.

Grayson took off his shoes, which was something Piper had always insisted on, picked up Stoli, and carried him to the back door. He gently set him down on the porch and watched the elderly dog walk slowly down the steps. Like Grayson, Stoli had changed quite a bit since Piper died. He slept more than he was awake, moved more slowly, and lay in places he never had before, like next to Piper's shoes in the closet.

I wonder how long it will be until Stoli leaves me too.

Later that night, Grayson settled into his favorite spot on the couch, sipping a scotch on the rocks and watching the History Channel. Stoli, sensing the loneliness in the room, waddled over, jumped into Grayson's lap, and made himself comfortable.

The dog on his thighs and the heat of the whiskey hitting his throat kept his body warm, but his heart felt cold as he looked at Piper's recliner. Suddenly, his mind flashed back to his encounter with the new professor earlier that day, and the book he had been captivated by.

I wonder why Piper gave me that book. I'm sure I still have it somewhere...

He gently moved Stoli from his lap and set his drink on the cherry end table. He made sure to slide over a coaster—another thing Piper had always insisted on. The ice clinked against the glass due to the abrupt departure from his fingers. Stoli, a bit unsettled, resorted to circling a few times before plopping down in a new spot on the patterned upholstery.

Grayson walked deliberately down the beige carpeted hallway like a man on a mission. To convert one of the spare bedrooms into a home office, they had floor-to-ceiling bookshelves installed on the wall behind his desk shortly after moving in. Being both a bookworm and a philosophy professor, he had no problem filling the regal mahogany shelves completely. Because of the sheer volume of books, it took Grayson a while to peruse all the shelves. After coming up empty, he decided to check the cabinets on the bottom. About to give up, he noticed an old green book sandwiched in the corner. This edition of *The Imitation of Christ,* battered from the previous owner, was frosted in a layer of dust. He used his index finger to separate it from its neighbors and carefully opened it to the first chapter:

> **We must imitate His life and manners, if we would be truly enlightened and delivered from all blindness of heart. Let it then be our chief study to meditate on the life of Jesus Christ. (Bk. 1, Ch. 1)**

His eyes moved over the text, but it failed to pierce his heart. He read it a couple more times, but the words flew around like hummingbirds with nowhere to land.

Frustration from the entire day began to take over, and Grayson decided it was best to go to bed. He tucked the book under his arm like a football, flipped off the lights, and headed toward the living room. Stoli opened his eyes but didn't lift his head as Grayson set the book on the coffee table with a thump.

I'll try again tomorrow.

Grayson prepared for bed and slipped on the red flannel pajamas that had been a Christmas gift from Piper. She used to store them with the holiday decorations, but now he wore them year-round, despite the fact they were unseasonably warm for an Idaho summer.

He ambled over to the bed and pulled back the rose-embroidered comforter and matching sheet. For the first time ever, he wondered if it was strange for a single man to have floral decor in his bedroom. The thought was too exhausting to entertain, so he climbed in and looked longingly at the side that always stayed made. He leaned over and kissed Piper's pillow, a gesture that might have seemed silly, but one that made him feel less alone. As he lay there, he thought about all that had transpired that day. If he believed in God, gratitude for protection from that bolt of lightning would have taken the form of a prayer rising like incense, but instead, he thought about how sucky the day had been as the scotch softly rocked him to sleep.

Chapter 3

Over the next few weeks, Grayson tried to adjust to his life as a retired professor. The last evidence of summer had come and gone, and the fall semester was in full swing.

Grayson had been spending more time at home, but he didn't like being there during the day. It was a constant reminder of the changes in his life, and he wasn't sure he was ready to accept them.

Each time he walked past the coffee table, he saw the green book staring back at him. Occasionally, he opened it and began to read, but each time, it hit him with the same empty feeling as it had the time before.

Why doesn't this do anything for me?

Throughout this time, he continued his daily trips to the Cozy Roaster. Not only did he enjoy escaping from the house, but the students' presence brought him life, and the occasional coursework question gave him purpose. Even though he found himself to be useful at the coffee shop, he struggled with having so much time on his hands. Occasionally, he was asked to compose letters of recommendation, like the one he had recently written for Lucy. But with no more papers to grade, no more office hours, no more boring committee meetings, he had time. So. Much. Time. He used to dread some of the responsibilities of his job, but now he felt empty without them. When thinking about retirement, he had always looked forward to having time and freedom to dive into intellectual pursuits on his own terms, but now he found himself disinterested.

One crisp autumn morning, he walked into the Cozy Roaster and noticed that it was busier than normal. It was obvious the semester was well underway as the students were swarming like honeybees, fueled by pheromones, caffeine, and test anxiety.

"Hi, Dr. G! How's it going?" Lucy asked with a smile as she began to make his vanilla double espresso.

"Oh, I'm okay. It's crowded in here today, huh? It looks like my chair is just about the only spot left."

"Yeah, we've been swamped all morning," Lucy marveled as she worked the espresso machine effortlessly and smoothly; she could make his drink with her eyes closed. Lucy had always been a quick learner, and barista training was no exception. She was the best in town and entertained customers with artistic foamy designs she had learned to hand pour on top of their lattes.

"Here you go, Dr. G. Enjoy!"

Grayson thanked Lucy, grabbed his espresso, and headed for the leather chair. As soon as he sat down, Matthew walked in through the front doors. He had a presence about him that brightened the room. Grayson watched as he ordered at the counter and scanned the shop for a place to sit. Lucy pointed toward the supply closet where the last-resort folding chair was stored, and Grayson predicted he was about to have company.

Matthew smiled as he set down the chair in front of Grayson. "Dr. Rogers! A pleasure to see you again."

"Likewise. How's life at the university treating you, Professor?

Matthew chuckled. "I'm still getting used to that title! After 10 years of studying, I like the sound of it." He smiled. "To answer your question, I love it here! Although I'm not surprised. I knew any place where Grayson Rogers taught for 35 years would be an excellent institution."

Grayson smiled, thinking about how much he had enjoyed those years.

Matthew opened his satchel and pulled out his copy of the book that had been haunting Grayson for weeks.

Oh no, not that book again.

Grayson debated whether to say something, and then blurted, "You know Matthew, I'm not sure what you see in that book. I tried reading it, and I can't even get past the first page. But maybe it's me. Maybe it's because I'm not really into Christ."

Matthew looked pensive. As a professor of theology, he had heard comments like this on more than one occasion. "Ah, so you think Jesus was a liar or a lunatic?" he said with an engaging grin.

Grayson was a bit taken aback by the harsh choice of words, but after years in education, he could recognize the start of a scholarly discussion when it slapped him in the face. "I'm not quite sure what you mean, but I can see you're about to tell me." Grayson chuckled. He hadn't conversed like this in a while, and he needed the jolt of a mentally stimulating discussion more than he needed the buzz from the mug in his hand.

"C. S. Lewis once said that there are only three possibilities regarding who Jesus was. He was a liar, a lunatic, or Lord. The first option is that Jesus wasn't the Son of God and knew it: this would make him a liar. The second option is that Jesus wasn't the Son of God, but thought he was: this would make him a lunatic. The third, and only other option, is that Jesus was who he claimed to be..." Matthew paused and gestured for Grayson to complete his thought.

"The Son of God."

"Exactly!" Matthew tapped the book on the table between them for emphasis. "Through all my years of research, I have concluded that there IS a God and that he is all-knowing, all-powerful, all-good, all-loving, and also in control of everything. Nothing happens outside of His will."

Grayson thought for a moment about this explanation. It certainly made sense from a logic standpoint. Jesus didn't exhibit the personality traits of a lunatic, and a liar would essentially have to be a lunatic to go through a torturous crucifixion over a claim that wasn't true. He could also conclude it was an unlikely possibility that a liar or lunatic could be skilled enough to convince others to devote their entire lives and suffer their own torturous deaths to spread his untrue gospel. But if there was a God, why didn't he answer his and Piper's prayers?

In the 3 years prior to her death, Piper had begun to show more interest in the Catholic faith she had grown up with. She even started going to church again. *A lot of good that did her. She was rewarded with stage IV cancer.* After her diagnosis, they both prayed incessantly for weeks. Piper's prayers were coming from a place of faith; Grayson's were coming from trying to please his wife and figuring it couldn't hurt. But after her death, he was convinced that *if* there was a God, he wasn't listening and definitely didn't care about him or his late wife.

"Matthew, if there is a God, as you say there is, and he is all-loving and all-good, why would he *allow* my wife to die?" Grayson said somberly.

"Dr. Rogers, I know this doesn't help take away the pain, but God has his reasons for everything, and some things we won't understand this side of heaven. Suffering is part of our existence in this world because of the presence of sin and the brokenness that comes from it. All of us suffer in this life in some way…" Matthew's eyes got a little glassy, and he quickly changed the subject. "Enough about suffering, though. I've been thinking about something ever since we first met, and I'd like to run something by you. I think we can help each other." Matthew paused, seeming to wait for confirmation from Grayson.

Grayson stroked his chin with intrigue, "Continue…"

"Perhaps it's more than a coincidence that your wife gave you this book that you've never read, and it *just happens* to be the book that I'm designing a unit around, and that changed my life," Matthew said. "It's almost like us meeting here was an act of divine intervention!"

Grayson silently scoffed at divine intervention, the idea of a big guy in the clouds placing Matthew in *his* chair after practically striking him with lightning.

Matthew's voice switched to a more persuasive tone as he continued, "There is a reward for both of us here— sort of like a symbiotic relationship. This book could really help you, and I could use the help of an experienced professor. I want this unit to be transformational for the students, just like you talk about in your book, *Extending Beyond the College Classroom*! I purposely designed it with an application component, but I won't know whether it works when implemented unless I have someone try it, and I would love for that someone to be you. I would get your honest feedback to help with my course development, and you'd hopefully get the benefits of a transformation like I had. What do you say...will you be my guinea pig, Dr. Rogers?" Matthew asked with an enticing grin.

He couldn't believe that Matthew was going to design a course around *The Imitation of Christ*. Certainly, the students would find it just as hard to read as he had. But on the other hand, Matthew's enthusiasm was contagious, and Grayson appreciated that he was planning to take his advice.

Matthew reminded Grayson of a younger version of himself. He had the same passion for inspiring students, but he also possessed something Grayson never had, a peace and light about him that were almost palpable. Being in Matthew's presence made him wonder if it was possible for him to obtain that sort of aura after all that he had been through.

Could this book help me?

Grayson thought about how boring and empty his days sometimes felt. He would love to have something to *do* again. He thought about Piper. As he did, the stab of guilt from never reading the book resurfaced and settled as a lump in his throat.

Piper, in remembrance of you...

"Ok, I'll do it!"

Matthew looked almost as surprised to be hearing the words as Grayson felt saying them.

"But.... I reserve the right to drop this "class" at any time," Grayson joked.

"Trust me, you won't want to," Matthew smirked as he quipped back. "Let's meet back here at 9:00 on Monday for Step 1."

Matthew finished the last swig of his tea, packed up his satchel, and headed for the door. He seemed to be making another quick getaway—almost like he wanted to leave before Grayson had a chance to change his mind.

Chapter 4

Grayson got up Monday morning with a little more pep in his step. Something about the prospect of being a student again invigorated him, even if he wasn't looking forward to the subject matter.

He packed his briefcase with the usuals—his wallet, computer, phone, and planner. As he walked past the coffee table, he grabbed the green book and opened it. Again, he read slowly:

> **We must imitate His life and manners, if we would be truly enlightened and delivered from all blindness of heart. Let it then be our chief study to meditate on the life of Jesus Christ. (Bk. 1, Ch. 1)**

This time the phrase "blindness of heart" stood out to him. He had always considered himself an intellectual and often felt enlightened, yet here he was struggling. Struggling with this book. Struggling with the loss of his wife. Struggling with his retirement. He started to consider whether his world was out of whack, or whether *he* was.

Am I suffering from blindness of heart?

He closed the book and slipped it in his briefcase, slung the leather strap over his shoulder, said goodbye to Stoli with a soft pat on the head, and set out toward the Cozy Roaster.

Shortly after the two professors arrived, Matthew pulled out a neatly organized blue binder that had "I.C.U." printed on the spine.

"What's I.C.U.?" Grayson asked with intrigue.

"*The Imitation of Christ* Unit!" Matthew exclaimed.

Grayson noticed the binder contained labeled dividers as Matthew gently turned to the one that read, "Step 1."

"Alright, let's get started, shall we?" Matthew asked excitedly.

"I'm as ready as I'm going to be," Grayson teased tentatively.

"Ok, so I have designed the unit into 7 weeks. Each week contains one step related to imitating Christ. For each step, the students will have excerpts from the book to meditate on, a saint who lived the content with perfection, and activities to apply the concepts to their daily lives."

Sounds easy enough.

Matthew took a sip of his tea and continued, "This book was written almost 600 years ago, in the 1400s by a monk entrusted with instructing novices in the monastery where he lived. It has inspired, and helped to form, numerous saints during the last 6 centuries. It's not a typical book that can be digested quickly. It's extremely important, Dr. Rogers, if you want this to be beneficial, to proceed slowly and deliberately. *The Imitation of Christ* is full of timeless wisdom that bears new fruit each time you read it."

Grayson took a sip from his mug as Matthew continued. "Like that espresso you are sipping on, this book is designed to be savored. Because of this, I'm going to ask you to focus on one step for an entire week. In the classroom, my plan is to lecture about the topic and then send students home with what I'm giving you. I believe this application piece will be where transformation begins to happen, so that is what you will be testing. I'm going to ask you to share your progress and any ideas you have for improvement. Sound doable?"

Grayson, having completed much more complicated work in the past, said "I think I can manage that, Professor."

Matthew passed him a piece of paper with simple instructions for the first week entitled "Step 1: Examination of Conscience."

"Look, I've got to run to class. Here's my number. Text me if you have any questions. Let's meet here at the same time each week, if that works for you," Matthew said as he packed up his belongings.

As soon as the young professor left, Grayson pulled out his copy of *The Imitation of Christ* and opened it to the excerpts listed on the lesson for the week. He tried to sip on them slowly.

> **Diligently examine thy conscience, and to the best of thy power cleanse and purify it by true contrition and humble confession: so that there be nothing weighty to give thee remorse and hinder thy free access [to God]. (Bk. 4, Ch. 7)**

The glory of a good man is the testimony of a good conscience. . . Keep a good conscience and thou shalt always have joy. A good conscience can bear very much and is very joyful in the midst of adversity. A bad conscience is always fearful and uneasy. . . Never rejoice but when thou hast done well. The wicked never have true joy, neither do they feel internal peace, because "There is no peace to the wicked, saith the Lord." (Bk. 2, Ch. 6)

I don't think I'm wicked, but where's the joy?

Grayson tried his best to imprint the words on his heart. He really wanted to give this process a try, for Matthew, for the students, and especially for Piper.

The next part of the lesson was watching a video about St. Ignatius of Loyola. The video discussed his life and focused on how *The Imitation of Christ* impacted his journey to sainthood. Grayson was shocked that a man like Ignatius, who was a worldly soldier, womanizer, gambler, and swordsman, filled with vanity and pride, could become a saint. The man had engaged in a plethora of sinful activities prior to his conversion, and even had a police record!

After completing the video, Grayson looked again at the handout from Matthew. The last section was the application assignment. Grayson was to meditate on those sections from the book every day and practice Ignatius' Examen of Conscience for 15 minutes before going to bed.

Grayson neatly tucked the handout inside the front cover of his planner. The idea that a good conscience was linked to joy was intriguing to him, and he quite enjoyed learning about St. Ignatius of Loyola. He wasn't so sure about examining his conscience, though. He hadn't spoken to God since Piper was sick, and the thought of doing so stirred up unpleasant memories.

To squash a rising anxiety, he decided to leave the coffee shop early and go for a stroll around campus. He needed time to think about all this, and walking tended to get his juices flowing.

Although he normally ate his lunch at the Cozy Roaster, he packed up his things and asked Lucy for an ice water and a turkey panini to go. She seemed pleasantly surprised he was doing something different, and he could tell by the look on her face she was intrigued about what could be enticing him out of his daily routine.

"See you tomorrow, Lucy," Grayson chimed as he left the building.

As the door shut behind him, he couldn't help but wonder if he was starting to open another.

Chapter 5

As Grayson stepped out of the coffee shop, the brisk autumn air tousled his silver hair. With his carryout order in tow, he set off down the road, wondering where this journey with Matthew would take him. His mind hopped around like a frog across lily pads, landing abruptly on the video that he had watched just minutes ago.

He couldn't help but see himself in the story of the fascinating saint. In 1520, when St. Ignatius was 30, he had been struck by a cannonball during a battle, and his leg had been shattered. The doctors did such a poor job resetting the bones that they protruded hideously and caused Ignatius to limp for the rest of his life. Although Grayson hadn't been struck with a war weapon, he had been dealt a blow this last year—one that left his heart shattered, instead of an appendage. And while his injuries weren't visible to the naked eye, he sure felt like he had been limping, barely able to get from point A to point B.

Ignatius studied books about Christ while he was recovering and in bed immobilized. And now here I am, sort of doing the same. Maybe Ignatius and I have more in common than I originally thought.

As Grayson strolled past all the beautifully restored historic shops downtown, he wondered if *The Imitation of Christ* could transform him the way it did Ignatius. A grumbling sound escaped from his stomach, and his mind switched gears.

I think it's time for lunch.

One of the best parts of the town of Kempis was the park a couple blocks from the square. Although it was in the middle of town, it was quite large and provided the perfect escape to nature that the university community craved.

Grayson eyed a picnic table under a pavilion next to the pond and headed toward it. Out of his left ear he could hear the squeaky sound of a shopping cart approaching. He snapped his head toward the peculiar sound and noticed a man he had seen dozens of times before. He didn't always have the cart, but today he pushed around a yellow blanket, a camo backpack, and a couple bags of random items. There weren't many homeless people in the area, but this man had been hanging around for a few years.

Grayson had noticed him many times but never offered him more than a passing glance. Even though he always carried cash, he never considered giving money to the man, assuming he would spend it on alcohol or drugs.

Grayson plopped down on the wooden bench and carefully unwrapped his turkey panini. The smell of melted cheddar and the Cozy Roaster's homemade honey mustard sauce made his mouth water. As he was about to take a bite, a scene from the video he watched earlier flashed in front of his eyes.

Ignatius gifted his clothes to a poor man when he gave up his old life. Should I give this man my lunch?

Grayson was startled by the question that danced in his mind. He couldn't remember the last time he had sacrificed something he wanted for someone else. His stomach protested the thought with an audible grumble, but Grayson remembered the questions he was going to have to answer that night.

He set the food down and pulled out his planner. He glanced at the bottom of the page Matthew had given him. "How did you act?" and "When did you love?" stood out like two Great Danes in a room full of corgis. After a silent debate between his stomach and his brain, Grayson quietly wrapped up his meal and walked over to the homeless man.

"This is for you," he said as he passed the paper bag and bottle of water into dirty, tired hands.

A gap-toothed smile swept over the man's wrinkled face as a "God bless you!" emerged from his lips.

A warm feeling spread across Grayson's body.

Could this be joy? Grayson pondered as he walked away with an empty stomach and a slightly less empty heart.

Later that night, Grayson crawled into bed with Matthew's handout. His eyes scanned again to the bottom of the page. With a resolve to follow the Examen of Conscience protocol exactly as written, he set his phone timer for 15 minutes.

"Quiet your mind. Relax your body. Turn your attention to God." As he read the words aloud, he tried to hush the rushing thoughts and unclench his tense shoulders. He read the next instructions.

1. Recall you are in the presence of God.

2. Reflect on your day, thanking God for everything.

3. Ask the Holy Spirit for help.

This is the part he had been dreading. Memories from the hospice center, where he had last prayed, began to flood in.

This never did me any good before.

He thought about just closing his eyes and going to sleep when he remembered the promise he had made to Matthew and to Piper.

I at least need to try.

He thought back on the events of the day—his meeting with Matthew, the video about St. Ignatius, his stroll through town, and the homeless man. He pressed through the feelings of discomfort that were taking over, took a deep breath, and began.

"Okay, God...if you're even there...It's me, Grayson." He stammered along uncomfortably as Stoli watched curiously from his bed in the corner.

"I know it's uh...been a while, but I'm still here. Thank you for...everything?... I guess. Holy Spirit, if you exist...I could use a little help...I suppose."

This is torturous.

Stoli moaned subtly in agreement, but Grayson continued. He glanced back at the paper and scanned over the questions.

Examine your day:
- How did you act?
- How did you feel?
- Where did you fail?
- When did you love?
- Are your habits negative or positive?
- Could you have used Jesus's help today?

He tried to answer each question thoughtfully. He recalled how he had acted, felt, and loved. He also reflected on his habits and the ways he had failed. This stirred up a mix of emotions and made him question his choices since Piper's death.

Maybe tomorrow I'll skip the scotch on the rocks.

He read on:

> Reconcile yourself to God. Resolve to avoid bad situations. Petition your needs for tomorrow.

"God...*this feels like I'm talking to myself.* I'm sorry for the ways I failed today. I will avoid bad situations...or try to. If you're going to send another poor person around lunchtime, I could use a nudge to order a second sandwich. Goodnight. I mean... Amen."

He looked at his phone and noticed he still had 7 minutes to go.

Are you kidding me? That felt like an hour!

For the remaining time, Grayson closed his eyes and tried to continue to think about the reflection questions. When the timer dinged, it felt like he'd been saved by the bell. He set the paper on the nightstand next to the book Piper had given him.

St. Ignatius had this book in the room with him on his deathbed. What do all these people see in this book!?

Chapter 6

Before Grayson knew it, the first week had come and gone. As each day passed, the examination of conscience got a little easier and a little less awkward. Grayson was surprised to find that by the end of the week, he didn't completely hate his new nightly routine. Something about the practice seemed to give him more clarity, direction, and purpose. Talking to a God he wasn't sure existed was still a little uncomfortable, but he could see positive effects beginning to filter into his daily life.

Grayson strolled into the Cozy Roaster for his scheduled meeting with Matthew, anticipating what the next week would hold.

"Dr. G! I can't thank you enough for that letter of recommendation!" Lucy was beaming with excitement. "I submitted my applications last night. I was really humbled by what you wrote about me!" She blushed as he walked toward the counter.

"I just hope my letter doesn't dissuade them," Grayson joked.

"You're so funny, Dr. G."

"Seriously, any doctoral program would be lucky to have you."

Lucy smiled while making his vanilla double espresso. Today she had her hair twisted into a side braid that accentuated her youthful glow.

Grayson grabbed his coffee and set out toward the familiar corner, where Matthew was waiting for him in the folding chair.

"You could have sat in the leather," Grayson offered as he thought about how he would answer the *When did you love?* question later that night.

"Oh, no!" Matthew said, throwing his arms into the surrender position. "Lucy filled me in that *that* chair has been unofficially reserved for you, for all eternity."

Grayson chuckled as he sat down. "Well, I am their best customer, you know. I started coming here about 3 and a half *decades* ago, when Joey and Rachel Murphy first opened the place."

Grayson got a nostalgic look in his eyes as memories started to flood in. "Many things have changed since then, but one that hasn't, is my love of coffee." He held up his mug with a smile. "I've had to add an extra shot over the years, though. Don't want the students to see the ol' prof fall asleep in his chair." He laughed before he took a swig.

The two scholars shared a smile. "I see that you drink tea," Grayson said nodding toward Matthew's mug.

"I do." Matthew replied quietly. He stroked the white ceramic with his thumb as his eyes drifted toward the window. "I used to drink coffee but decided it was best to switch to something decaf. Most places don't have decaf coffee ready, so tea is easier."

Grayson wondered why anyone would ever voluntarily give up caffeine but decided it was best not to pry. He considered changing the subject to Matthew's family, but that didn't go well last time, so he opted for another direction. "Have you found a nice place to live?"

"Yes. I went with a 12-month rental, since it'll be quite a while before I have tenure," Matthew smiled. "It's in Glendale."

"Glendale?" Grayson seemed surprised. "That's a 45-minute commute! There are so many rentals close to campus. Could you not find anything you liked here?"

Matthew's eyes began to get that frantic look again as he fidgeted in his seat. "I actually didn't even look here..." his voice trailed off. "But, hey! Let's discuss how your first week went."

It was obvious Matthew didn't want to talk about his drink or his housing choices. Not knowing what else would be "safe" to talk about, Grayson sighed in relief as the conversation diverted to scholastics.

"Actually, it went better than I expected. The examination of conscience was hard at first, but I started getting the hang of it toward the end of the week. Knowing I had to answer those questions at the end of the day encouraged me to make different choices. I noticed people more and chose kind actions that normally wouldn't have crossed my mind." Grayson paused and smiled. "I'm surprisingly looking forward to what you have in store for me this week."

"That's great, Dr. Rogers! It sounds like the process is beginning nicely." Matthew pulled out his blue binder and turned to the next labeled divider. "After one examines one's conscience, one inevitably finds areas that need a little shoring up. Which leads us to the next step. *The Imitation of Christ* highly recommends leading a virtuous life, so Week 2 will focus on virtues."

Grayson was familiar with the virtues from a philosophical perspective. "There are many virtues, Matthew. I hope you aren't going to ask me to implement ALL of them in 7 days," Grayson chuckled.

"Oh no. I'm going to have you concentrate on just one. When asked what the four cardinal virtues were, St. Augustine replied, 'Humility, humility, humility, and humility.' He also was quoted as saying 'Humility is the foundation of all the other virtues hence, in the soul in which this virtue does not exist, there cannot be any other virtue except in mere appearance.'"

"Sounds pretty important to start with humility then," Grayson agreed.

"Since humility is the foundation of all the others, it's best to make this our next priority. In class, however, I will lecture on the four cardinal virtues and give students suggestions on how to cultivate those when they are ready. Matthew snapped open the prongs of the binder and passed Grayson a page-protected sheet.

Cultivating the Four Cardinal Virtues

1. **Prudence** - Helps you discern the best choice in every circumstance.

   We must not be easy in giving credit to every word and suggestion; but carefully and leisurely weigh the matter according to God. Alas, such is our weakness, that we often more readily believe and speak of another that which is evil than that which is good! But perfect men do not easily give credit to every report, because they know a man's weakness, which is very prone to evil, and very subject to fail in words... (Bk 1, Ch. 4).

   Actions: Pray over your encounters with others in your daily life and reflect on your actions. Do not act rashly or cling obstinately to your opinion. Do not spread around gossip. Reflect on and take responsibility for the words that come out of your mouth.

2. **Justice** - The constant and firm will to give what is due to God and to others.

    Action: Respect the rights and dignity of everyone, even when you are upset.

3. **Fortitude** - The moral virtue that allows you to conquer your fears, resist temptation, and face the trials placed before you. It is a higher form of courage because God is involved supernaturally in assisting your soul.

    Actions: Practice patience—this will help you exhibit and strengthen your fortitude. Exercise constancy—be consistent in your work, knowing whatever you do is for the glory of God. Think about a way you can strive for greatness in your life. Start working toward it and pray for God to guide and strengthen you.

4. **Temperance** – Moderates our attraction for pleasures and desires. Once cultivated, you will be able to use material goods in a way that is best for you and doesn't lead you to sin.

    Action: Avoid or moderate excess in your life (food, drink, material items, screen time, etc.).

"That looks great, Matthew! I love how you are familiarizing them with the virtues, but focusing the application on the foundational one." Grayson marveled at how much work the young professor had already put into this unit.

Matthew handed Grayson a crisp sheet of paper that read "Step 2: Cultivating Virtues" and instructed, "Here is your homework for the week. I've got to run. Same time next week?" Matthew slurped down the rest of his decaf tea and headed out toward campus with a wave, barely waiting for Grayson's affirmative response.

As a professor, Grayson had always approached the virtues merely from an academic perspective. Now, he wondered what would happen while he tried to grow them in himself.

"What can I get you for lunch, Dr. G?" Lucy asked with her trademark smile.

"I think I'll have a B.L.T. wrap--"

"And the sweet potato fries!" Lucy interjected loudly with a wink.

"You know me too well, Lucy," Grayson chuckled. "Either that or I'm just too predictable."

"You are definitely NOT predictable, Dr. G. I never would have guessed you'd *ever* offer your favorite chair to someone else. I about dropped my tray of dirty dishes when I overheard that."

"Ah," Grayson replied introspectively. "Well, I've been working on something with that new professor, and I'm already starting to notice some changes in myself."

"Those smiles I've missed are starting to come back, so whatever you're doing, keep it up," Lucy waved her finger like she was Grayson's mother giving him orders. "I'll have this right out for you," she grinned while walking away.

As the marriage of salty and sweet from the crispy fries mingled on his tongue, he glanced at his assignment for the week. Its structure was the same as the week before, so he wiped his hands on a napkin and removed *The Imitation of Christ* from his briefcase. Turning to the pages listed on Matthew's handout, he read slowly:

> The more humble a man is in himself, and more subject to God, the more wise will he be in all things, and the more at peace. (Bk. 1, Ch. 4)

> If there is good in you, see more good in others, so that you may remain humble. It does no harm to esteem yourself less than anyone else, but it is very harmful to think yourself better than even one. The humble live in continuous peace, while in the hearts of the proud are envy and frequent anger. (Bk.1 Ch.7)

Grayson wondered what living in continuous peace would look like. He couldn't remember the last time he felt tranquil. The last year had been stressful and lonely, the exact opposite of what the book was describing.

Grayson took a bite of his B.L.T. and looked at the next section as he chewed. This week he was supposed to watch a video about St. Philip Neri. He pulled out his laptop and diligently clicked through the listed steps and pressed play.

Like St. Ignatius of Loyola, St. Philip Neri was a big fan of *The Imitation of Christ*. He lived in the 16th century in Italy and was a humorous, charitable, and joyful priest who practiced the cardinal virtues. He became known as the "Apostle of Joy" because he was witty, funny, and *fun*. Here was another man who didn't fit the *saint mold* Grayson had fabricated in his head. St. Philip Neri showed that holiness and joy could be lived simultaneously.

Grayson closed his laptop and couldn't remember the last time he had *had fun*. It must have been sometime before Piper's diagnosis, over a year ago. He glanced at the bottom of the paper to discover the action piece for the week.

This week, try to do the following every day:
1. Acknowledge your nothingness and think better of others than yourself.
2. When you feel prideful, remember your gifts come from God and not from your own ability.
3. Find an opportunity to laugh at yourself.

As Grayson finished his lunch and packed up his belongings, he began to feel strangely motivated by St. Philip Neri and the hilarious stories from the video.

Laugh at myself, eh? Hmm...what can I do today that would give me an opportunity to laugh at myself? Grayson stroked his chin as he brainstormed.

He considered what he had learned about the spontaneous, comical priest. To practice humility, St. Philip Neri would wear ridiculous clothes or walk around with half of his beard shaved off. The greater his reputation for holiness became, the sillier he wanted to seem. Grayson didn't have a razor or entertaining clothes in his briefcase, so he had to think of something different.

In a stroke of impulse, or insanity, the esteemed professor headed toward home to grab his car keys. He was going to the skating rink.

Chapter 7

Grayson rolled into the parking lot of The Pink Rink in his navy Lincoln Town Car. It was 12:30 p.m. on a Monday, so only a handful of cars were in the parking lot.

I think I can. I think I can. I think I can. Grayson repeated to himself like *The Little Engine that Could*.He whipped the wheel to the left and pulled into a spot close to the front door.

What am I doing here!? I must have legitimately lost my mind. Piper, I can only imagine how much you'd be laughing if you could see this. You'd probably be wondering whether to have Dr. Horton give me a psychological evaluation.

Grayson tucked his chocolate leather wallet in his back pocket and headed toward the building. He had passed this iconic structure hundreds of times over the years but had never been inside. He typically rolled his eyes at the gaudy 5-foot tall pink skate spinning on its axis outside the front doors, but today he slipped it a wink.

He swung open the glass door, and bells on a string announced his arrival.

"Welcome to The Pink Rink. Are you here to pick someone up?" A young woman chomping on gum, with rainbow streaks slicing through her black hair, greeted him.

Grayson glanced over at the few kids circling the floor and began to laugh at himself silently. "No ma'am. I'm here to skate."

The employee looked around like she was waiting for hidden cameras to pop out and someone to shout, "Smile! You're on Candid Camera!"

As Grayson approached the counter he read "Hayley" on her name tag and wondered if she went to the university.

Hayley looked at him like he had screws loose, and Grayson wondered if she was right. "Really? What size skate do you need?"

It's not too late to change my mind...

"Ten and a half," he blurted out. His voice was more committed than the rest of him.

"I also will need one of those." Embarrassed, Grayson pointed toward the white skating aides constructed of PVC pipes resting in the corner.

The girl laughed loudly, "Oh honey, those you can use for free." With a look that said, "*I can't wait to see this,*" she gave Grayson his total.

After paying in cash, he sat down on one of the pink benches to lace up his skates. Just as he was about to make his way to the mostly empty floor, a big yellow school bus rolled into the parking lot.

Grrrrrreat. A field trip! Just my luck.

Grayson spent the next hour shuffling his feet across the slippery floor, trying not to break a hip. He held on to the kid-sized PVC pipe contraption for dear life as second graders sped past him, pointing, and laughing. The two teachers scolded them for being rude, but it didn't do much good. Grayson looked like a baby giraffe trying to stand for the first time.

Nothing builds humility quite like being lapped and giggled at by kids one eighth your age as neon lights flash to the Bee Gees.

Despite the embarrassment, Grayson couldn't hold in his own laughter. Every time one of his legs tried to roll away or the PVC rescuer broke his fall, belly laughs erupted. The sounds (or sight) must have been contagious because every person in the building was laughing with him, or at him; he wasn't quite sure.

About the time the soreness started to kick in, he decided it was time to head toward the rink exit.

"Hey, Mister!" One of the kids shouted. "You're pretty cool. My grandpa would NEVER do *that!*" The boy's eyes got large as he extended his hand for a high five.

Grayson returned the gesture with a clap and thought about Matthew's assignment.

I am nothing. Think better of others than myself.

Grayson replied, "You and your friends are MUCH better than me. I'm horrible at this!"

"Yeah, you kind of are," the 7-year-old giggled.

His classmates skated over and formed a line like you'd see at the end of a Little League game. As Grayson scooted out, every single one of them gave him a high five.

They must be congratulating me for making it out of here alive. Grayson smiled and laughed to himself. *Piper, you were right, as always. Laughter really is the best medicine.*

"Nice job, Gramps. I had 9-1-1 on speed dial over here. Glad I didn't have to use it." Hayley teased as Grayson headed for the exit. "You come back now."

He carefully considered the suggestion. Perhaps he would come back sometime.

Later that night, Grayson planted his sore body in his over-sized leather desk chair. He stared at the plaques on his office walls and the books he had authored displayed on the shelves.

What does all of this mean? Are these things really from God and not from me?

Earning these accomplishments had felt amazing at the time, but now they just collected dust and reminded him of time spent away from Piper.

Grayson trudged to the closet and pulled out a large blue tote. One by one, he took each accomplishment of his career and buried them in the plastic tomb.

God, if you're there, thanks for giving me the intelligence, skill, and work ethic to accomplish all of this. If it came from you, I cannot claim the glory. The cost of my ego robbed me of precious time with Piper. Grayson looked around at the bare walls. Inspired by the amusing day, he pulled out his phone and ordered an 11 × 14 painting of St. Philip Neri from an artist on Etsy.

Well, that's a start. Grayson thought to himself as he headed toward the bathroom to get ready for bed.

Chapter 8

A week later, Grayson walked into the Cozy Roaster for his meeting with Matthew.

"Whoa, Dr. G! You're rockin' a new look!" Lucy's eyes widened as she looked him up and down. The always professionally dressed prof was sporting a white cowboy hat and blue jeans.

"Well, Matthew's been giving me these 'research assignments,' and one led me to take myself less seriously. What do you think? I picked up this beauty at the St. Vincent de Paul thrift store." Grayson tipped his hat to Lucy.

"You're living it, Dr. G. I almost took you for an Idaho ranch hand! You know, something's goin' on with you. I've never seen you so relaxed." Lucy began to whip up his vanilla double espresso. "By the way, I've got something *huge* to share. Have a seat, and I'll bring this right over."

Grayson headed toward his chair and sat down. As soon as he unpacked his briefcase, Lucy came bopping over with the coffee and a little too much excitement to contain. "Here you go, Cowboy," she joked as she passed him his mug and marveled at his hat.

"Enough! I want to hear your *huge* news."

Lucy's eyes sparkled as she paused for effect. "I got in! I can hardly believe it, I got in! I'm going to be *Doctor* Finley!

Grayson clapped his hands together and grinned from ear to ear. "I'm not surprised, Lucy! You're the best student I ever taught, and I mean that."

Embarrassed by his praise, Lucy shook her head. "You've done so much for me, Dr. G. Your classes, from freshman year on, and all I learned from you as your teaching assistant, your wise advice and constant encouragement—your letter of recommendation! I owe you so much!"

"You've worked extremely hard, Lucy. You earned this," Grayson beamed.

Their celebration was interrupted by a ding on Grayson's phone.

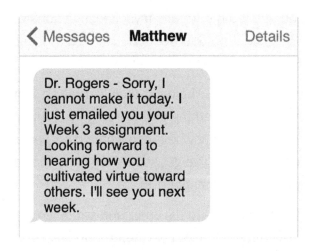

> ‹ Messages **Matthew** Details
>
> Dr. Rogers - Sorry, I cannot make it today. I just emailed you your Week 3 assignment. Looking forward to hearing how you cultivated virtue toward others. I'll see you next week.

"Matthew can't make it today. I guess I'm *riding* solo." Grayson said, still playing the cowboy. He was slightly annoyed with Matthew's cancellation without explanation.

That's strange. I wonder what came up.

"Hey Lucy, when you get a break, come back over to my office," Grayson joked. "There is something I want to talk to you about."

"Sure thing, Dr. G. I've got one in 15 minutes. Be back shortly."

Lucy practically pranced away as Grayson fired up his laptop. Matthew's email was waiting. "Week 3: Watching Temptation." He clicked to open it.

> Dr. Roger,
>
> Sorry, something came up!
>
> This week we are focusing on temptation. There is no way around temptation for anyone, even the virtuous. Everyone is going to have to step in the fire.
>
> **A man is never entirely secure from temptations as long as he lives, because we have within us the source of temptation, having been born in concupiscence [or state of sin and weakness]. (Bk. 1, Ch. 13)**
>
> Remember, no matter how hard you work at this, temptations are never going to end.
>
> **When one temptation or tribulation is over, another comes on; and we shall always have something to suffer, because we have lost the good of our original happiness [because of the fall in the Garden of Eden]. (Bk. 1, Ch. 13)**
>
> Good luck this week! Email me with any questions.
>
> Matthew
>
> Sent from my iPhone

Just as he was about to open the attachment, Lucy clunked the folding chair in front of him and sat down.

"Dr. G, I have to tell you, I love what Dr. Arcanum's project is doing for you. You seem so much happier lately."

"I think I *am* happier lately. The application piece has been so stimulating, and I think *The Imitation of Christ* meditations are growing on me. I haven't stepped this far out of my comfort zone...probably ever," Grayson said, recalling the Pink Rink escapade.

"Maybe I need to check this book out," Lucy pondered. "I should probably read it *before* I start my doctoral program. I'll be swamped with studying. I'm really excited, but I'll really miss you and even this place." She spread her arms as if to embrace the Cozy Roaster.

"You can always come back and visit. The world is waiting for you, *Doctor* Finley," Grayson winked.

"I'd love to come back, but I may not be able to afford to! This program is so expensive, and the fact it's far away just adds to the cost. I'm about to be so deep in debt that I'll be working every second I'm not studying."

"Well, this is leading nicely into what I wanted to talk to you about," Grayson looked from side to side like he was about to share something secretive.

"Lucy, you know it's been almost a year since my wife passed." Lucy nodded somberly. "But she and I have been working on something ever since she died."

Lucy's brow furrowed. "Huh? Ever since she died?"

"Yes. We had to involve attorneys and bring in big donors, so it took a while. But we wrapped everything up about 3 weeks ago."

"Dr. G, what are you talking about?"

"My wife's family was very wealthy. Before she passed, I

asked her what we should do with all the money that *nobody* knew we had. As you know, we have no children to pass it on to. Well, after watching me dedicate my life to educating young people, she had an incredible idea to set up a foundation."

Lucy cocked her head to the side, "A foundation?"

"Yes. A foundation dedicated to helping students pursue advanced degrees."

Lucy's face went blank.

"Lucy, I am going to propose to the foundation's board that our first jumbo grant be made to Lucy Finley. I am all but certain the board will approve."

He watched as Lucy's face exploded in joy and tears began running down her cheeks. She put her hands over her face, splitting her fingers so she could look at the man who had already done so much for her academic career.

"Dr. G, I'm speechless! How can I ever thank you enough?"

"You already have, Lucy," he said as he smiled warmly and gently patted her arm. "Just don't forget about me when you hit the big city and earn that fancy title. Just think that if you stay the course, you'll be a doctor *without* a lot of student debt to repay."

That afternoon, Grayson arrived home elated from surprising Lucy. Stoli, seeming to sense his unusually good mood, ran to get his favorite toy. Ten seconds later he came bounding in with a most unusual looking squeaky object.

On Stoli's 13th birthday, Piper gifted him a squeaky chew

toy with a plush mustache attached to it. She would laugh hysterically every time he played with it.

Seeing the toy in his mouth made him feel like she was back in the room. Tears formed in his eyes as he said, aloud, "Piper, we did it! You should have seen Lucy's face today."

Grayson went to the kitchen and opened the freezer. Piper used to have a homemade meal prepared when he arrived home from work, but for the past year he'd been living on microwave dinners. He looked through his selection of frozen food and opted for the Hungry-Man Country Fried Chicken meal.

Eight minutes later, supper was warmed, and he was ready to eat. He sat down in an oak Windsor chair at the kitchen table and pulled up his email. Swallowing a bite of steamy mashed potatoes, he opened Matthew's attachment and turned to the meditations for the week in the little green book.

> Fire tries iron, and temptation tries a just man. We often know not what we can do; but temptation discovers what we are. . . For first a bare thought comes to the mind; then a strong imagination; afterwards delight, and evil motion and consent. And thus, little by little, the wicked enemy gets full entrance, when he is not resisted in the beginning. And the longer a man is negligent in resisting, so much the weaker does he daily become in himself, and the enemy becomes stronger against him. (Bk. 1, Ch. 13)

Temptations are often very profitable to a man, although they be troublesome and grievous, for in them a man is humbled, purified, and instructed. All the saints have passed through many tribulations and temptations, and have profited by them; and they who could not support temptations, have become reprobates, and fallen away. (Bk.1, Ch.13)

Many seek to fly [from] temptations, and fall more grievously into them. By flight alone we cannot overcome; but by patience and true humility we are made stronger than our enemies. He who only declines them outwardly, and does not pluck out the root, will profit little; nay, temptations will sooner return to him, and he will find himself in a worse condition. By degrees, and by patience . . . thou shalt by God's grace better overcome them than by harshness and thine own importunity [or anxieties]. (Bk.1, Ch.13)

Three meditations seemed like a bit much for the week, but Grayson could see why Matthew selected them. The first describes how temptation works, the second explains how it can be beneficial, and the third instructs how to overcome it—all necessary information for the students.

Matthew had chosen St. Thomas More as this week's saint. Grayson was familiar with him from the 1966 movie, *A Man for All Seasons*, which had won five Oscars. Grayson smirked when he thought about the fact that Matthew hadn't even been born when it was released, and had likely never heard of it.

Grayson pressed play on Matthew's video and wondered if he'd learn anything he didn't already know from the classic. *A Man for All Seasons* takes place in sixteenth century England. More was a devout Catholic, the Lord Chancellor, and an intimate friend of Henry VIII. King Henry wanted to annul his marriage to Catherine of Aragon and marry his mistress, Anne Boleyn. Pope Clement VII would not grant the annulment, and Thomas, a brilliant lawyer, supported his ruling.

Henry defied the pope, married Anne Boleyn, broke away from the Catholic Church, and wanted More to take an oath acknowledging the legitimacy of Anne Boleyn as queen and elevating his position as king to include head of the Church of England. As an incentive, Henry VIII offered More an elevated position, which guaranteed a life of luxury. More had a choice to make: take the oath or be executed. Talk about temptation! More chose the path of integrity and was beheaded. No amount of wealth or power would have changed his mind because he knew what was right in the eyes of God.

Matthew's video confirmed the movie's accuracy, and Grayson learned that St. Thomas More also admired *The Im-*

itation of Christ and guided his life by it. During a time when few people owned books, and even fewer owned more than one, he believed it should be one of the three books everyone should own. Through consistent practice and habitual action, he became adept at resisting temptations.

The video also made sure to mention that the reason St. Thomas More developed the strength to overcome the big temptation was by resisting and overcoming smaller ones throughout his life.

Grayson scanned his eyes to the bottom of the page to see what the week had in store.

1. Resist as many temptations as you can this week.

2. Each evening, journal about how the day went.

3. Reflect on the temptations you fled from and how it was profitable to do so.

4. Contemplate the temptations you failed to overcome and discuss how those affected you.

5. Come to class ready to discuss.

Grayson thought about what that discussion piece would be like. College students face so many temptations, temptations that are much different than what he faces as a 64-year-old man.

Grayson finished the last bite of his warm sweet apples and threw the plastic tray in the trashcan. He considered what he should be trying to avoid this week. He didn't feel like he faced any big temptations. He had been a partier in his younger days but had calmed down after meeting Piper and had always remained faithful to her. They had never splurged on cars, or fancy jewelry, or a country club membership. He considered that his workaholic tendencies had always been a temptation, but now he didn't even have that.

Matthew said that temptations continue for as long as a man lives. What am I facing now? It seems like a bunch of little things. The tendency to just pass the time, or rather, let it pass me by is a huge one.

Grayson looked around. For the first time in months, he noticed a thin layer of dust covering everything in the living room, a few plants on the verge of death, and Stoli's nose prints all over the window. His eyes settled on the battered old cover of the green book.

When she gave this to me all those years ago, I said "I'll take a look when I have time." I never had time. I never made time. Matthew treasures this book, but me? I let it languish on the shelf for years. There must have been a reason Piper gave it to me for our anniversary, but I ignored it.

Grayson sighed. He considered what his life would have looked like, and how his marriage would have been, if he had met Matthew sooner. He knew though, deep down, he never would have agreed before now to do something like this.

He yawned as he thought about what his journal entry would look like tonight. He decided to skip the scotch and his nightly History Channel binge. Instead, he grabbed a bottle of Windex and a dust rag.

Chapter 9

Grayson woke and dread consumed him. He was supposed to have met Matthew yesterday but had received another "I can't make it today" text. This time, instead of emailing the assignment, Matthew had asked to reschedule for today. Grayson agreed, but now that today arrived, he was thinking about sending his own cancellation text. It wasn't that he didn't want to see Matthew. He didn't want to see anyone.

Today was the 1-year anniversary of Piper's death, and Grayson felt like staying home. He knew if he did, he might resort to crying and drinking whiskey all day. As inviting as that sounded, he decided to follow in St. Thomas More's footsteps and resist the temptation. Plus, he knew that fresh air and see-ing other people would be good for him.

It was a cool, cloudy November morning as Grayson made his way to the Cozy Roaster. He saw himself in the dead leaves that crunched under his feet—vibrant and colorful the week before and lifeless now.

As Grayson swung open the heavy door, he noticed some-thing unusual. The seats around the big table against the wall normally occupied by hard-working students, were filled with men in suits.

Grayson moved quickly to the counter. "Lucy, what's going on over there?"

Lucy shook her head and looked down. "Oh Dr. G, I'm so sorry. Things are about to change," she let out a deep breath.

"The Cozy Roaster's been sold. Those are the new owners over there with their lawyers. None of us saw this coming. They told us they're going to close the shop at the end of the week for renovations." She paused. "They said that it will be 'a whole new Cozy Roaster.'"

Lucy sighed as she took in the stunned look on the face of a man who had been coming to the Cozy Roaster for longer than she'd been alive.

"They plan on reopening right after Thanksgiving break to capitalize on final exam season."

With all the students cramming, the last few weeks of the semester were always extremely busy, and therefore extremely profitable. Grayson stood in stunned silence. He didn't know what to think. This news was *devastating*.

Of all the days to get this kind of news, it had to be this one.

"Lucy, I really could use that double espresso," Grayson replied dismally.

Lucy gently smiled. "You got it, Dr. G."

A couple minutes later as she handed him his coffee, she presented him with a card in a pastel green envelope. "I know what today is. Piper would have been so proud of the work you are doing with Dr. Arcanum." She came around the counter and gave him a daughterly hug.

"I can't believe I had to be the bearer of such horrible news, especially on this day." She wiped a tear as it dripped down her cheek, and Grayson held back one of his own.

"Thanks Lucy. I don't know what I'm going to do without you next year."

Grayson tried to compose himself as he tucked the card in his inside coat pocket and headed toward the familiar corner. Matthew was seated in the folding chair waiting for him.

Matthew spoke first. "I heard the news. I hope they don't ruin the place!"

Grayson sighed. "35 years, Matthew. 35 years of coming here. It's hard to believe."

"I can see the shock written all over your face."

"Well, to be honest, it's not just the shock about the Cozy Roaster," Grayson frowned. "I'm all out of sorts today. It's the 1-year anniversary of my wife's death."

Matthew shook his head. "I didn't know that. I'm so sorry, my friend."

"I was doing so well with this little experiment, Matthew. You should have seen me the last couple of weeks. I put on a cowboy hat, went roller skating, and have all but given up my nightly scotch on the rocks. And then today, it feels like I'm back at square one." Grayson swallowed hard. "I don't know if this feeling is ever going to go away. Decades of joy, friendship, and intimacy suddenly gone. Suddenly changed. And now everything is changing. The one mainstay I thought I could count on will never be the same." Grayson glanced over at the table full of men in fancy suits.

"I'm so sorry, Dr. Rogers, I'm not sure what to say." Matthew bowed his head, and the two men sat in silence for a few moments.

"Even in the midst of our messes, God never changes," Matthew paused. "I hope you'll cling to that someday."

Grayson considered the suggestion. "I just don't even know what to believe in anymore." He threw his shoulders back and let out a deep sigh. "Well, Matthew, we've got some work to do, and I could use a distraction. What do you say we get started?"

Matthew nodded and grabbed his satchel. He pulled out the binder labeled "I.C.U.," along with his treasured, gold-letter–embossed copy of *The Imitation of Christ*. "How did last week go?"

"It was a bit harder than the first 2 weeks. I had difficulty figuring out what my temptations were. I know I used to struggle with being a workaholic, and robbing Piper of my time. She gave me this book, and I just let it gather dust all these years. I really regret that."

Matthew listened intently and respectfully. He had no idea that the professor he had long admired was battling with so much. He waited as Grayson let out a deep breath and took a long sip of his coffee.

"Professor, with all due respect, I think you are still struggling with temptation more than you realize."

Grayson tilted his head. "I'm not quite sure what you mean."

Matthew paused and spoke in a soft, sympathetic voice, "Listening to what you're saying, it seems to me that you're being tempted to despair, to become despondent, to see darkness where there is still quite a bit of light."

Grayson shifted uncomfortably in his chair and took a moment to reflect on Matthew's words. "There doesn't seem to be much light...especially on a day like today."

"Dr. Rogers, you're dealing with some genuine issues, and I don't want you to go all *Pollyanna* about it, but Satan wants to take away your hope. That's how he works. When we are weak, he attacks."

"Well, I guess you can say he's attacking. So, what's the remedy for this? How do I find the light?"

"I'm glad you asked because one essential remedy is prayer, and that just happens to be the next step in the curriculum," Matthew grinned like a salesman who had the cure to all of Grayson's ailments. "As I mentioned, these steps naturally build on one another. You first examine your conscience, then you begin to cultivate virtue. After you become aware of the temptations around you, you better start praying." Matthew handed Grayson the handout for Step 4 and then continued.

"Now Dr. Rogers, I know you're a philosophy professor, but I want you to think of this really simply. Prayer is just conversation with God. People think prayer is hard because they overcomplicate it, but it is truly one of the easiest things in the world."

"Well, it doesn't *feel* easy. I mean, I've come a long way since Day 1, but it definitely doesn't feel like one of the easiest things," Grayson scoffed.

"Look, many people overthink it and let their heads get in the way. God made you, has been with you every second of your life, knows everything about you, loves you, and always wants what is best for you. God is your best friend; just remember that." Matthew took a sip of his tea. "In class I will talk with students about finding prayer practices that foster their friendship with God. We will discuss that effective prayer is more about the person who is praying than it is about God. God loves every type of prayer because each one brings the person praying closer to him. Even the *effort* to pray brings closeness."

Grayson took in the words. He wondered how he could have a best friend he wasn't sure existed. Up until now he'd been going through the motions of Matthew's assignments. They had been transforming him in a positive way, but he still didn't know what he believed. He found Matthew's liar, lunatic, or Lord argument compelling, and he'd been thinking about it a lot lately. But he wasn't ready to say Jesus was the divine Son of God. While he certainly saw positive changes, he wasn't convinced that God was the change-maker.

Could my effort to pray really be bringing me closer to God, even though I'm not convinced he's there?

"A few quick things before I have to jet off: Christ prayed con-stantly and in numerous ways. To truly imitate Christ, you must do as He did and pray like He prayed. As I'm going to teach the students, all kinds of prayers are needed in our lives, and one size doesn't fit all. For the application piece, I'm going to focus on The Jesus Prayer and a fun little acronym. I think you'll like it," Matthew smiled and got up. "Oh," he stopped. "Since the Cozy Roaster will be closing this weekend, let's meet back the Monday after Thanksgiving Break. In the meantime, why don't you use the extra time to read more of *The Imitation of Christ*?"

Without waiting for Grayson's reply, Matthew grabbed his satchel and waved to a group of students on his way out the door.

Grayson exhaled loudly. *What a day*, he moped. He couldn't believe that the next time they met, his beloved home away from home would look completely different.

Chapter 10

As Grayson walked home that afternoon, he glanced at the paper Matthew had handed him.

> If thou knowest not how to meditate on high and heavenly things, rest on the Passion of Christ, and willingly dwell in His sacred Wounds. For if thou flee devoutly to the Wounds and precious stigmas of Jesus, thou shalt feel great comfort in tribulation; neither wilt thou much regard being despised by men, but wilt easily bear up against detracting tongues. (Bk. 2, chap. 1)

> A lover of Jesus and of truth, and a true internal man, that is free from inordinate affections, can freely turn himself to God and in spirit elevate himself above himself, and rest in enjoyment. (Bk. 2, Ch. 1)

Grayson could see that Matthew was building on the virtue of humility from last week. As he kept reading, he saw he was supposed to watch a video about St. Dominic Savio. He found an unoccupied bench and pulled it up on his iPhone while slipping his headphones in.

He learned about the Italian boy born in 1842, who was the youngest person to be canonized without being a martyr. He was only 14 when he died of tuberculosis. *The Imitation of Christ* was one of his favorite books, and he would pray for the grace to keep his heart like Mary's, free from every impure desire.

Grayson was amazed that such a young person could live such a pious life. Dominic was known for getting so absorbed in prayer that he would lose all track of time. One day he had been missing from breakfast, class, and lunch, when they finally found him in the sanctuary. He was standing behind the main altar as still as a rock. One of his hands rested on a bookstand, the other was pressed to his heart, and his face was gazing at the tabernacle. When spoken to, he said, "Is Mass over already?" He had no clue it was 2 o'clock in the afternoon.

On another occasion, Dominic was found talking by himself in the sanctuary as if he were talking to an invisible person. "Yes, Lord, I have said it before, and I will keep on saying it, I love you and I want to love you all my life. If you see that I am about to commit a sin, make me die first! Yes, death first, but not sin!"

Talk about using prayer to effectively squash temptation and sin!

When the video ended, Grayson glanced at the bottom of the page:

Pray The Jesus Prayer as often as you can:

The Jesus Prayer:

Lord Jesus Christ, son of God, have mercy on me.

Before you go to bed each night, study for your A.C.T.s.

A = Adoration (adore God)

C = Contrition (tell God you are sorry for your sins)

T = Thank Him (thank God for all He has done)

S = Supplication (ask God for what you need)

Grayson found the acronym amusing. *Most of the students will have recently taken the ACTs for entrance into college. This will be easy for them to remember.*

Later that evening, the weight of the day hit Grayson like a meteor. He was sitting in his familiar living room, but everything looked different. The table wasn't just a table; it was where he had shared thousands of meals with his soul mate—his soul mate who was never coming back. Piper's chair wasn't just a recliner; it was the place where she had sat every night for most of their marriage. Now it sat empty. The green book with the battered cover wasn't just a book that Piper read and passed down to him; it was a thoughtful gift from the love of his life, which he had never cared to open until she was gone.

He ran his wrinkled hands over the cover, and the wave of guilt from never making the time to read it returned to his heart again. He slowly opened to the first book titled "Thoughts Helpful in the Life of the Soul."

For the next hour, Grayson plowed through it. The directly applicable advice that poured from its pages strummed a chord in his soul that had never been played. He read aloud to Stoli who lay in his lap.

> True peace of heart, then, is found in resisting passions, not in satisfying them. There is no peace in the carnal man, in the man given to vain attractions, but there is peace in the fervent and spiritual man. (Bk.1 Ch. 6)

I never really resisted my passions. Sometimes I pursued them with reckless, overindulgent abandon.

> What good is it to live a long life when we amend that life so little? Indeed, a long life does not always benefit us, but on the contrary, frequently adds to our guilt. (Bk. 1, Ch. 23).

The words pierced Grayson's heart like a dagger. St. Dominic Savio's short, pious life was in sharp contrast to the long guilt-ridden one he was immersed in.

He looked at his watch and decided he had time to read Book Two before bed. As he approached the end of the first chapter, he became paralyzed by a paragraph underlined in red ink:

> A spiritual man quickly recollects himself because he has never wasted his attention upon externals. No outside work, no business that cannot wait stands in his way. He adjusts himself to things as they happen. He whose disposition is well ordered cares nothing about the strange, perverse behavior of others, for a man is upset and distracted only in proportion as he engrosses himself in externals. (Bk. 2 Ch. 1)

When he finished reading, his eyes moved to a handwritten note on a blank page. He recognized the handwriting immediately.

Grayson, there are more important things than work. You're more than a professor. You're deeper than that. I hope that someday you'll see this as clearly as I do.

I love you,
Piper

Tears instantly poured down Grayson's face like a dam being released. He slammed the book shut and threw it on the floor. He turned his head to the side and covered his brow with his hand. The guilt and sorrow swept him up, carrying him away like a riptide current.

How could I be so unaware? How many times did she try to say something like this to me? How many times was I deaf to her words? She gave me this book because she knew I read more than I listened, but all I did was let it gather dust and focus on my work. I always thought we'd have plenty of time later. I was wrong. So very wrong.

Grayson's tears showed no signs of stopping as he began to let out audible sobs.

I've got to be with her.

Grayson got up and grabbed a fleece jacket and his car keys. The 10-minute drive to the cemetery was eerily silent. He parked and followed the stark, moonlit stone path to where Piper's body lay.

When he found the familiar gravestone, he collapsed to his knees.

"Piper, my dear, I'm so sorry." Grayson sobbed. "You always wanted what was best for me, but I was so blind. I thought I was doing what was best for us and thought there'd be time *later.* How did it all go by so fast?" Grayson spoke to the granite as if it were his wife.

"I feel terrible for the countless times I chose work over you, work over rest, work over...everything. It's all my fault. There's so much more that I could have done. So much more *we* could have done," Grayson wiped the hot tears with the sleeve of his jacket.

"I'm sorry I never read this book while you were here." Grayson clutched the green book in his clammy tear-covered hands. "I had so many opportunities to pick it up, but I never made the time. I let it collect dust on the shelf and you never pushed me. You knew I wanted to do things my way."

"I'm so sorry, Piper," Grayson sobbed. "I'm so, so sorry. Will you ever be able to forgive me?"

The sound of his weeping filled the chilled air, but the silence from the tombstone was deafening.

Chapter 11

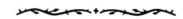

Grayson stood in front of his liquor cabinet and glanced toward the wall clock he inherited from his grandfather. The gold pendulum swung back and forth just like his consistency the past few weeks. One day he was following Matthew's protocol and incorporating prayer into his daily life, and the next he was drinking scotch with his morning Cheerios.

It was 2 p.m., but he decided it was 5 o'clock somewhere, so he pulled out the familiar bottle. He had no wife, no job, no Cozy Roaster, and no reason to stay sober.

It was Thanksgiving, and Grayson wasn't feeling like he had much to be thankful for. He had come so far with Matthew, trying to imitate Christ, yet the anniversary of his wife's passing and the Cozy Roaster changes had completely thrown him off track. He felt as if he'd taken ten steps forward and twelve steps back. Now, he wondered if he needed the twelve-step *program*.

He'd been trying his best to be faithful to the process, but was he just going through the motions? He would pray through A.C.T.S. on nights he was sober enough to do so, but his heart felt far from the task at hand as he bounced between numbness and anger.

The ice crackled as he poured the potent liquid into his glass. He knew he couldn't keep this kind of behavior up. He had a meeting with Matthew in 4 days at the "new" Cozy Roaster.

I have got to get myself together. Maybe I should try that Jesus Prayer again.

Grayson had memorized the prayer, even though he hadn't been saying it every day. In exasperation he said, "Lord Jesus Christ, Son of God, have mercy on me."

Okay there, I said it. I don't feel any different. I guess I'll say it again.

This time he said it a bit louder, "Lord Jesus Christ, Son of God, have mercy on me."

C'mon, God, have mercy on me. Do I deserve this hell that I'm going through?

Raising his voice a bit more, he cried "Lord Jesus Christ, Son of God, have mercy on me."

Nothing...Okay, I'm going to say this prayer one more time. Are you listening?!

This time he was almost yelling, and his teeth were clenched as he growled, "Lord Jesus Christ, Son of God, have mercy on me."

Grayson sat with his eyes closed, but his breathing remained heavy. Inside he was seething.

Grayson downed the remainder of his scotch and then poured another without much thought. Half an hour later, he passed out on the couch and slept until morning.

Grayson woke up to Stoli repeatedly nudging his hand with his nose.

What time is it?

Grayson groggily looked toward the clock. A quick glance was enough to remind him it was the morning after Thanksgiving. Normally by this time, Piper would have had all the Christmas boxes out and Michael Bublé crooning on the record player.

Piper used to love decorating for Christmas. If Grayson would let her, she would have put the Christmas tree up in October. He always insisted she wait until Thanksgiving was over because he hated the idea of one holiday infringing on another. As soon as the sun would rise on Black Friday, she could be found decked out in her holiday gear and spreading Christmas cheer throughout the house.

Grayson would typically spend the day preparing the final reviews and exams for his courses. Now he wished he could go back in time and help her hang the garland. If he could have Piper back, he would let her keep the tree up all year long if she wanted.

The thought of sitting around the house for another day was just too much to swallow, and Stoli's stare was begging for attention. Grayson popped an aspirin and chugged a glass of water, hoping that would take the edge off the lingering headache from yesterday's binge. He quickly scarfed down a chocolate chip granola bar and grabbed Stoli's leash.

"C'mon, old buddy. Let's go for a walk."

At the sound of the "W" word, Stoli started wagging his tail. Even though the corgi was elderly, his long slender body wriggled with excitement. He still loved walks, and if they went slow enough, he'd be able to manage a trip to campus and back.

The day was unseasonably warm as they made their way toward the university. On school breaks, the campus was a place of solitude, and there were plenty of benches to take breaks if they needed one.

Just as Grayson and Stoli were sitting down to take a rest in front of the science building, a familiar voice boomed from behind them.

"Hey, Dr. Rogers! Who is your little friend?"

Grayson jumped.

He had never seen Matthew wearing shorts.

The young professor sat down on the bench next to Grayson and was startled by the professor's exterior. His mentor had dark circles under his eyes and uncombed hair. He looked like he hadn't slept in days or been to hell and back, he wasn't quite sure.

"This is my dog, Stoli." Grayson picked the corgi up and set him on the bench between them.

Matthew let Stoli sniff his hand and then he began gently stroking his back.

"I'm surprised to see you here, Matthew. What are you doing here on your Thanksgiving break?"

Matthew held up a stack of folders in his hand. "I forgot some things I needed to work on this weekend. What about you? Are you thinking of coming back to teach?" Matthew joked.

Grayson shook his head and muttered, "Who'd want an old sad-sack professor like me in a place like this?"

Alarmed at the despairing response, Matthew set down his folders.

"Dr. Rogers, you really seem down. Is there anything I can do?" Matthew offered. He assumed Grayson was having a hard time coping with the anniversary of his wife's passing.

Grayson let out a big sigh and looked down at the ground, pausing while he debated whether to open up to the young professor.

"When I was your age, Matthew, I thought I had the world by the tail. I was happy, successful, nothing could get me down, just like you..."

"Hmph, sometimes what you see on the outside isn't the whole story," Matthew interrupted.

"I'm not quite sure what you mean."

Matthew let out a sigh of his own. "You have no idea what I've been going through. Most folks don't." He paused and looked around to make sure the men were completely alone. "Dr. Rogers, my wife is in a rehabilitation center."

Grayson's eyes grew wide as he tried to process this information. He thought back to Matthew's strange response at their first meeting when he asked if he was married.

Matthew continued. "It's kind of a long story, but it's my fault. My wife was working two jobs, sometimes covering overnight shifts for more pay. She was exhausted all the time, but she persisted, saying it would end as soon as I finished my doctorate. One day, a coworker offered her a pill and told her it would help her stay awake and alert. That one pill turned into two, and two turned into three. And then before she knew it, she was addicted."

Grayson sat there in stunned silence as he listened intently.

"On her way home one night, she was driving erratically and was pulled over. The officer found a cache of pills, and long story short, she ended up sentenced to a court-ordered rehabilitation center...in Glendale."

Grayson stroked Stoli's back as he suddenly realized why Matthew had chosen to rent a home 45 minutes from campus, and why he had chosen to give up his own addictive substance—caffeine.

"I felt horrible, Grayson. I was studying so hard for this PhD, and I wasn't bringing in any money. We have a 2-year-old son who needed to eat, and my wife ran herself into the ground to provide for us...something I should have been doing. I was so consumed in my own endeavors; I didn't even notice how bad she was struggling." Matthew's eyes began to water a bit as he put his hands in his jacket pockets.

Grayson sat stunned. He had no idea Matthew was going through so much. He looked like he had it all together. "How long is she going to be away?"

"It's an intensive program. She's in for a year."

Grayson took a deep breath as he wrapped his mind around this vibrant professor, who exuded peace and joy, silently dealing with so much. "Matthew, I had no idea! How have you been able to hold everything together?"

"Well, it definitely hasn't been easy. Starting a new job with such a long commute while being a single parent, and of course missing my wife, has been hard. I hired a full-time nanny to take care of Christopher, but things happen. A few times she called in sick, which is why I had to cancel our meetings.

Grayson suddenly felt bad for being upset about the cancellations. "I had no idea what you were going through." Stoli groaned as if in sympathy.

"Well, you know, that book we've been talking so much about? It's really helped me get through this."

Grayson looked surprised. "I know you said the book was transformational, but how can a book help you through something like *that*."

"Well, it truly is a life-changing book. *The Imitation of Christ* is so unique because it is direct, instructional, applicable, and relevant to all our lives. It's not just transformational once; the practices can continue to be built upon over a lifetime."

Grayson sat in silence as Matthew continued.

"On top of all the surface things like missing my wife, becoming a single dad, and trying to find a job close to Glendale, I was dealing with tremendous guilt. I felt like it was all my fault because I wasn't providing. And now my son was going to have to live without a mother. But on top of that—deeper than that—there were all the questions like 'Why is this happening?' 'What does it all mean?' 'Why me?' I wrestled with these questions for weeks. I was in a downward spiral and had nobody to turn to. There was certainly no one in my professional life I could talk to. I didn't even want them to know."

Grayson thought back through their conversations to Matthew's strange reactions to his questions, and it all became clear.

"So, I dove back into *The Imitation* for help. That book has a strange way of always containing exactly what you need to read." Matthew smiled. "Anyway, on one of my lowest days, I opened it up and decided to follow its advice and go to Eucharistic Adoration."

Matthew looked over at Grayson to see if he knew what the term meant.

"Grayson, I know you left the Church during your college days, but you may remember that Jesus is truly present—Body, Blood, Soul, and Divinity—in the Holy Eucharist. In that chapel, spending time adoring our Lord, like St. Dominic Savio, I could see the Light even though there was darkness all around me. I would read *The Imitation* in the chapel, and it transformed my life. I became eager to go to confession, and soon thereafter, I confessed my sins. I laid out my guilt and shame for failing to provide for my family, which contributed to my wife's addiction and resulting crime. I was absolved of my sins, and the guilt and shame disappeared. I resolved to become the husband and father that God wanted me to be."

Grayson was amazed to see exactly how transformational *The Imitation of Christ* had been for this young man, and he longed for that kind of lasting transformation for himself. He would give just about anything to be free of the guilt he felt now that Piper was gone.

"You know Matthew, I can see how this book has been life changing for you. I felt like I was starting to experience some of that the first few weeks, but the anniversary of my wife's death, the Cozy Roaster renovation, and the lonely holiday season seem to have sent me in a downward spiral. I wonder if it's too late for me to get back on track."

"Grayson, with God, it's never *too* late."

"So, where do I go from here?" Grayson asked somberly.

"You know, Grayson, I had that same question." Matthew picked up his satchel from the stone bench and pulled out the familiar book. He read:

> **"'In the Sacrament of the Altar, Thou art wholly present, my God, the Man Christ Jesus; where also the fruit of eternal salvation is plentifully reaped, as often as Thou art worthily and devoutly received. And to this [Sacrament] we are not drawn by any levity, curiosity, or sensuality; but by a firm faith, a devout hope and a sincere charity. (Bk. 4 Ch. 1)'"**

"Because of this passage, in addition to receiving the Lord at Mass, I began spending a portion of every day in front of him in that little chapel. The intimacy with my Lord and my God helped me to know beyond a doubt that he would bring me through all of this." Matthew smiled. "It just so happens that the next step in the process is embracing the Sacraments."

Grayson let Matthew's words sink in for a moment. He had never been to adoration before and hadn't participated in the sacraments in over 20 years. "But Matthew, I did horrible with

Step 4. Praying was so hard for me. I tried, I really did, but it didn't work for me. I'm not sure I'm ready to go on to another step when I didn't successfully the complete the last one."

Matthew leaned forward, thinking deeply. "Hmm. Well, what if you tried a different kind of prayer? Go into the silence of the Adoration Chapel, and in there, you will discover a kind of prayer that worked for me."

Grayson considered this, "How would it be different? Don't you just pray in there, too?"

"People always think of prayer as talking *to* God, but a vital part of prayer is learning how to *listen* to God talking to us. You might begin very simply, by just saying 'Okay, God, I'm suffering. Here I am.' Then just shut up, sit back, and listen."

Grayson was intrigued. He'd never tried listening for God's voice. Any time he prayed he'd just done all the talking, and most of the time, he was asking God for something. Now he wondered what that might have felt like for God.

Matthew chuckled, "So Grayson, we basically just covered Step 5. I read you the meditation for the week, and the application piece is to go to adoration."

Matthew reached into his bag and pulled out a book titled *Visits to the Blessed Sacrament*.

"This was written by the saint for this step, St. Alphonsus Liguori. He quotes *The Imitation of Christ* in here. You can hang on to this until our next meeting and do a little research on him if you have some spare time."

Grayson chuckled, "I have all the time in the world, Professor."

Matthew stood up. "I've got to get going. I only have a babysitter for one more hour. But let's not meet on Monday, since we basically had our meeting now," Matthew smiled. "Let's meet the following week instead. Does that sound good?"

"That sounds great, Matthew. Thanks for sharing all of this with me today. I'm really thankful for you...more than you know."

Matthew patted him on the back, "I'm always here for you, Doc," Matthew said lovingly. "I hope you know that."

The two men parted ways, and on his way home Grayson sent up a sincere prayer.

Thank you for bringing Matthew into my life.

Chapter 12

Grayson skimmed through the book by St. Alphonsus Liguori, in which Liguori called the Eucharist "our heaven on earth," and figured he could really use some of that.

When Piper had her reversion a few years ago, she started frequenting a church on the outskirts of campus. The priest assigned there later ministered to her in the hospice center and gave her Last Rites. The thought of walking into the place where Piper had her funeral made his stomach turn, but it was close to home, and they had an Adoration Chapel that was open 24/7.

He found it ironic that he started his day popping an aspirin for a hangover and was now ending it in church.

He moved under the cover of nightfall to the main doors of St. Teresa of Avila Catholic Church. Relieved to find them unlocked, he stepped inside where the scent of residual incense greeted him.

Looking around, he noticed the Adoration Chapel on the left side of the vestibule. He hesitantly approached and slowly opened the chapel door. It was a small room, seating only about fifteen people, and no one else was there.

His eyes were magnetically drawn to the gold structure with sun-like rays centered on the altar. Although he had never been to adoration, he had done enough research that afternoon to know he was staring at a monstrance, a vessel that displayed a consecrated Host of the Body of Jesus Christ.

He moved slowly down the short aisle and sat in the first pew on the left. Although he felt a bit awkward not having done this before, he was strangely comfortable.

Okay, God. Here I am. I'm broken and unconvinced, but I'm here.

It didn't happen right away, but as he sat there in silence with his eyes closed, a strange peace swept over him. The warmth spread over his body, and the nagging tension he had been hanging onto for months slowly began to ease. He felt an almost tangible release of anxiety as a sense of calmness swept over his heart.

One thought led to another as his mind drifted back over the last 35 years of his career. Images flashed through of the books he had authored, the comradery he had shared with the coworkers, and the thousands of students he had both taught and learned from. He saw the faces of those he inspired, those he tolerated, and those he loved, like Lucy Finley.

Suddenly, Piper's handwritten message popped into his head. He could see her distinctive script and almost hear her voice: "You're more than a professor." The words ricocheted through his mind as scenes from the past rapidly filled his head—sipping wine with friends, dinner parties with the neighbors, weekend walks through town. Routine things. Normal things. Nothing special.

But oh, how special those things really were. How many times did I cancel our plans in order to work? Piper never seemed to complain, but maybe that's because she was...Piper. What an unselfish companion God gifted me with. I didn't deserve her.

A thought stuck in his mind. "Go check out the books." *Could it be the Holy Spirit?*

Grayson opened his eyes and headed toward the white bookshelf at the back of the room. On top were marble statues of Mary, the Mother of God, and St. Joseph. The three shelves were filled with religious books that had likely been donated by parishioners. Not sure which one to grab and unaccustomed to praying, he whispered under his breath, sheepishly, "God, show me the book you want me to read."

As his eyes scanned the shelves, he saw one book sticking out in the middle. The spine read, "Story of a Soul. The Autobiography of St. Thérèse of Lisieux." It seemed to stand out, so he grabbed it and sat back down in the pew.

As he began to peruse the book, he learned that the secret to her sanctity was doing *everything*, even the smallest thing, for the love of God. She referred to her life as "The Little Way."

Isn't that interesting, I always wanted The Big Way. Big Ideas. Big Books. Big Accolades. But this is preaching the opposite.

Grayson thought about how Thérèse lived her life to imitate Christ. *What if I imitated Christ the way she did? What if I tried to do everything, big or small, out of love for God instead of love for myself?"*

He took his thumb and shuffled through the pages like a card dealer at a Vegas casino. He stopped on one and the words made him gasp, "For a long time I had nourished my spiritual life with the fine flour contained in the *Imitation of Christ*. It was the only book which did me good, for I had not yet found the treasures hidden in the Holy Gospels. I always had it with me, to the amusement of my people at home."

Another saint inspired by this book!

He suddenly had the urge to open his own copy. He turned to a random page and could hardly believe his eyes:

> Nothing is sweeter than love; nothing stronger, nothing higher, nothing more generous, nothing more pleasant, nothing fuller or better in Heaven or on earth; for love proceeds from God and cannot rest but in God above all things created. (Bk. 3, Ch. 5)

Grayson knew this could not be a mere coincidence. He didn't *just happen* to get a desire to look at a book. He didn't *just happen* to choose one about a saint doing small things with great love. She didn't *just happen* to have a deep devotion to the book he'd been studying. And he didn't *just happen* to open this book and turn to a passage about love proceeding from God. Grayson had a feeling deep down in his soul that the events had been divinely orchestrated.

He put the book down and sat in a pew directly in front of the monstrance.

If there isn't a God, what could the source of love be?

"God, are you going to speak to me?" he whispered quietly. A few moments later he had an urge to re-open *The Imitation*, and turned to another random page:

> Thou alone speak to me, and I to Thee; as the beloved is wont to speak to his beloved, and a friend to entertain himself with his friend. (Bk. 4, Ch. 13, referring to Ex. 33:11)

Shuddering, he closed the book and fell to his knees. He gazed at the Sacred Host contained in the monstrance and knew in his soul he was staring at the Lord. A prayer welled up within him, and he couldn't keep the words from pouring out. The words were familiar, but for the first time ever, he prayed them from his heart. "Lord Jesus Christ, Son of God, have mercy on me." He repeated the prayer and then said it again as tears freely flowed.

The next evening, before the Saturday vigil Mass, Grayson went to Confession, the Sacrament of Reconciliation, for the first time in 45 years.

Chapter 13

Grayson woke up the next morning feeling like a clean slate. The grief was not gone, but he had tremendous peace. The feeling of knowing that Matthew was right, that there really was a God and that he had a chance of seeing Piper again someday, lifted his spirit to a place he didn't know it could rise.

As he was eating a bowl of oatmeal and watching the morning news, his phone dinged. It was a text from Lucy:

Grayson's heart dropped to his stomach. The Cozy Roaster was set to have its grand reopening tomorrow. Grayson had been debating whether to go, so he responded hesitantly.

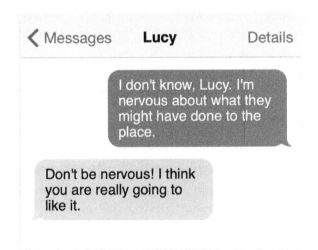

Grayson thought about changes the new owners might have made that he would actually like, but not even one came to mind.

Maybe it's better to see it before it opens to the public. The fewer people there to see my disappointment, the better.

Grayson told Lucy he would meet her at 3 p.m. and opened the *Imitation of Christ*, hoping to stumble across something that would make him feel better; as usual, the pages did not disappoint.

> **Whensoever a man desires any thing inordinately, he is presently disquieted within himself. (Bk.1, Ch. 6)**

Whoa. I think I have felt so much stress over this change because my love for it is excessive. God needs to become my new Cozy Roaster.

Grayson began walking toward the square at 2:40 p.m. As he approached Main Street, he could see Lucy walking toward the shop from the opposite direction. She was wearing a new Cozy Roaster shirt with jeans. He marveled at her bright, radiating smile.

"Look, Dr. G, they left the sign the same!"

Grayson glanced up at the old familiar sign that he'd walked under almost every day for half of his life.

Grayson laughed and crossed his fingers, "Maybe they left the whole place the same!"

"Well, not exactly." Lucy couldn't stifle a laugh.

She pushed the door open, and Grayson followed her in. As he stepped inside, the familiar aroma of freshly brewed coffee and old books mingled with the scent of sawdust.

His eyes quickly moved to the corner where his comfortable chair had been positioned as if it were chained to the floor. The chair was *gone*. In its place was a four-top pub table with vintage padded chairs.

His heart sank.

Lord, help me to desire you more than the things of this world.

Searching for consolation, he pulled his favorite green book out of his briefcase and read:

> **When comfort shall be taken away from thee, do not presently despair; but wait with humility and patience for the heavenly visit, for God is able to restore thee to a greater consolation. (Bk. 2, Ch.9)**

Lucy noticed Grayson pause and look up something in the book he always had with him. "Dr. G, are you all right?"

"Yes, sorry. I just needed to remind myself of something. Let's continue the tour," he smiled.

As Grayson looked around the rest of the familiar building, he was pleasantly surprised. The place had an eclectic, old-school feel, punctuated by college-style zaniness.

The shop's colors had remained the same, but now old red bricks cascaded down toward the counter from the back corners of the wall. Thrift store rugs now warmed the original hardwood floors, and small antique lamps sat on every other table.

On the walls were dozens of oversized, black-and-white, framed photos that highlighted the history of the university and the Cozy Roaster.

What these new guys have done is impressive--other than deep-sixing my chair.

At that moment, a man in his early 40's with jet black hair and almond skin walked over. He was wearing a shirt that said *Drink More Coffee*. "Lucy, thanks for coming in early and bringing in our best customer." He extended his right hand. "I'm Eric, one of the new owners," he said warmly.

Grayson returned the man's handshake and complimented the renovation. "I was afraid you were going to turn this place into a glorified Starbucks, but it looks like you went for comfortable and homey instead."

"Well, that was the idea," Eric said, as he and Lucy both smiled. "Let me show you around."

Eric led the pair to the counter. Grayson was pleased to see that they hadn't replaced the iconic piece. Instead, they added an impossible-to-miss display board that read:

"This ancient counter has absorbed more coffee and overheard more joyful conversations than any other in this state."

Grayson chuckled and nodded as he looked at Eric. "That's really good."

The threesome walked over to a long community table, which

was obviously designed for group study. Its tabletop was covered by a collection of lids from metal food cans, glued together and encased under clear glass. A display board sitting in the middle of the table, read,

"If you're not drinking something, you're not really studying."

"Here's another table that I love," Eric said, moving to the left. It was a 3-inch–thick wooden table cut in the shape of an arrowhead. Benches for two were positioned on each side.

Grayson shook his head. "Eric, you've taken this place beyond my wildest dreams. You've managed to do the impossible."

Eric looked puzzled. "I'm not sure what you mean, Dr. G. The impossible?"

"You've managed to make the Cozy Roaster even more cozy!"

All of them laughed as Eric replied, "Well, thank you very

much. We've put a lot of thought and effort into it. I appreciate you coming in."

"I'm really glad I did." Grayson was truly happy he had decided not to stay away. "So, are you ready for the big reopening tomorrow?"

"Yes," Eric said. "We're almost ready, except we've got something to finish up over here." He led them to the corner tucked in the back of the room opposite the gray stone fireplace. The entire corner was covered by a thick construction-type tarp. "Hey, Buff!" Eric shouted toward the back room.

Instantly, a muscle-bound college student with dirty blonde hair appeared.

"Buff, did this corner get done this morning?"

"Actually, sir, we got it done last night."

"Perfect, let's see it," Eric smiled.

Buff reached up and with a hearty tug, ripped down the construction tarp. Grayson's eyes widened. A foot–high platform had been built into the corner. On the right side was Grayson's old leather chair. Across from it was a Scandinavian lounge chair with a cream cushion. In between the chairs sat a circular glass table with a mahogany wooden border.

Grayson almost fainted. He put his hand on Lucy's shoulder to maintain his balance. "I can't believe this," he stammered.

Lucy smiled. "Check out the inscription, Dr. G."

She pointed to the floor in front of the chair. Inlaid into the fine teakwood was a plaque:

Dr. G's Corner

This chair is reserved in perpetuity for Dr. Grayson Rogers, in acknowledgment of the thousands of students he has influenced, fueled by Cozy Roaster espressos.

Grayson couldn't remember the last time he cried like a baby in public, but he knew he would never forget this one.

Chapter 14

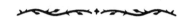

The next week, Matthew saw the renovations for the first time. "Dr. Rogers, I love your new corner! It's well deserved." Matthew took a sip of his tea. "The highlight for me is I no longer have to lug that folding chair out of the supply closet."

The two men shared a laugh.

Grayson took a sip of his mug that had "A yawn is a silent scream for coffee" written on the side. The new owners had gotten rid of all the ceramic white mugs and replaced them with a random assortment of entertaining mugs. Matthew was drinking from one that said "Tea-Rex" and had a picture of a tea bag with claws and sharp teeth.

"I want to get serious for a moment, Matthew. When you met me on that bench last week, I was really in a fog. And I have to tell you, your suggestion to go to the Adoration Chapel changed my life."

Matthew's face lit up. "That's great to hear! Tell more."

Matthew waited eagerly as Grayson took another gulp of his vanilla double espresso and repositioned himself in his old comfortable leather chair. For the next 20 minutes, Grayson told Matthew all about the profound experience he had in the chapel, including the providential discovery of St. Thérèse's "Little Way" and the moment he became convinced that Christ truly was the Son of God.

Matthew listened intently as Grayson continued, "I confessed the sins of my overindulgent ways and the harm they caused to Piper, and to myself. I had no idea the weight I was carrying. It felt so good to unload all that guilt and shame."

Grayson pulled out his copy of *The Imitation of Christ* and held it up. "Matthew, finally this all makes sense. I feel like I can actually live more and more like Christ by doing everything, even the little things, for the love of God. Not only did I go to confession, but I've started going back to Mass. Matthew, I know we have two steps left, but I had to let you know that you saved my life. Because of you, I may very well see my wife again someday."

The two men stood up and hugged as tears began to form in their eyes. Matthew broke the embrace abruptly, "Dr. Rogers! I just thought of something!"

He sat back in his seat and pulled out his binder and his own copy of the book. Grayson noticed the staggered, colored tabs they had already covered:

Step 1: Examination of Conscience

Step 2: Cultivating Virtue

Step 3: Watching Temptation

Step 4: Prayer

Step 5: Embrace the Sacraments.

"Step 6 is Working of the Holy Spirit! The Holy Spirit certainly moved in you."

"Monumentally!" Grayson agreed.

"As you were talking, it hit me. I need to rework my curriculum and make St. Thérèse of Lisieux the saint for this week."

"She would be a perfect choice." Grayson agreed. "She was

influenced greatly by *The Imitation of Christ,* and she immersed herself completely in the Holy Spirit."

"Exactly! She was plagued by illness most of her life. She was meek and weak, not rich, not famous, and not capable of making great sacrifices or performing great and glorious works. Yet she chose to remain a child in the eyes of God and performed all her duties with love and obedience, no matter how small they were. Her simplicity made her great, and she confirms we do not need to change the world to imitate Christ. She is an excellent exemplar, and since she helped to change your life, I know she can help to change the students' as well."

"I agree. So, what's next for me, Professor?" Grayson asked curiously.

"Well, I think it's safe to say you experienced transformation and that this process works!" In his best Kung Fu impression, he said, "I think I'm done with you, young grasshopper."

The two men laughed, and Grayson joked, "Professor, don't quit your day job." Matthew put his hand to his chest and opened his mouth pretending to be offended.

"So, Step 6 is Working of the Holy Spirit. What's Step 7?"

"The last step, yet truly the first step of many, is--living it! Imitating Christ!" Matthew shouted joyfully.

"Who is the saint you've chosen?" Grayson asked inquisitively.

"The saint is hopefully....YOU!"

Grayson looked confused.

"We are all called to sainthood, Dr. Rogers. So, the goal from here on out is to live with that in mind and grow in our own holiness every single day for the rest of our lives. We'll never be perfect, but we can move closer to perfection by practicing these steps every day. Over time, as you continue to imitate Christ, the transformation becomes not so much something you practice, but who you are."

Matthew continued, "Let's recap the entire unit. Step 1 was learning to examine your conscience. As the students practice this, they will become aware of their internal desire to be with God. They will be more able to embrace virtue and see where it is missing. Step 2 focuses on cultivating the virtues, especially humility, because a virtuous life helps you ward off temptation. Step 3 is where they learn they can't battle temptation alone and can use temptations to become closer to Christ. The best way to do that is through prayer, which leads to Step 4. In that step the students practice prayer, which is critical to all the steps. As they pray, they will become closer to Christ, and that closeness will bring a desire to experience the sacraments. In Step 5 they learn to embrace Christ's gifts that provide us with His grace, especially the Eucharist. In Step 6 they immerse themselves in the Holy Spirit, which happens naturally when you are truly applying the other five. And then lastly, Step 7 concludes the unit with the students seeking to imitate Christ. Throughout the unit they will have seen how saints are great models for us to try to become saints ourselves."

Matthew read a section from the book:

> I will walk in faith, strengthened by the examples of Thy saints. (Bk. 4, chap. 11)

Grayson nodded. "I love this, Matthew! That is a major call to action at the end. I am confident this unit is going to be *transformational* for your students. Nicely done, Professor!" Grayson lifted his coffee to cheers and the two men clanked their mugs together.

Chapter 15

As the end of the semester approached, Grayson and Matthew continued their weekly meetings. Over the course of 2 short months, they had become great friends.

On Lucy's last day, shortly before Christmas, Grayson strolled into the coffee shop.

Lucy immediately began to make his espresso as he handed her a neatly wrapped gift with a silver bow on top.

"Merry Christmas to my favorite student," Grayson smiled.

"Oh, Dr. G, you shouldn't have! You've already given me so much." Lucy lifted the small package wrapped in red and green plaid paper.

"It's just a little something I know you will love, and it's sort of a going away present, too."

She carefully ripped the wrapping paper and peeled it away from the gift. Inside was a brown leather book with gold embossed letters. She ran her fingers over the words, "*The Imitation of Christ*."

"Thanks Dr. G! I've been meaning to read this." She smiled. "You've changed so much these last couple of months." Tears began to form in her eyes. "I was so worried you were never going to go back to the old you. But the new you is a hundred times better!" She came around the counter and hugged him tightly.

"I'm going to miss you so much."

"I'm going to miss you too, Lucy Finley. This book will help you change the world, or at least change yours."

A couple of days later, Grayson walked into St. Teresa of Avila Catholic Church for Midnight Mass. As the choir sang Christmas hymns, Grayson marveled at how far he had come since this time last year.

A year ago, he spent Christmas Eve drinking his sorrows away in a decoration-free home, and this Christmas he had received the greatest gift of all: *Peace*. Peace from knowing that he was truly loved by a God who knows him completely. Peace from knowing Jesus is truly the Son of God and died for him. Peace from the hope of seeing Piper again someday. Peace that came in the form of a battered, dust-covered book. Peace from imitating Christ.

Epilogue

Four months later, with spring in the air, Grayson walked with pep in his step to Piper's gravesite in the cemetery.

"I brought you some flowers, Honey," he smiled as he placed a bouquet of fresh-cut roses on Piper's gravestone.

"I have so many great things to share with you, but I don't want to take up too much of your time." Grayson couldn't help but chuckle at the kind of humor Piper used to love.

"Matthew's wife, Lindsay, completed her rehabilitation program. She hasn't used in a year and just got released. Matthew beamed when he told me how great it was to feel like a family again." Grayson's smile got bigger as he pictured what their reunion must have been like.

"I also heard from Lucy yesterday! She said that thanks to our financial gift she doesn't have to work two jobs. With more free time, she ran into a priest on campus who just happened to be a fan of *The Imitation of Christ*. Can you believe she's interested in becoming Catholic? Maybe I'll tell her to research St. Lucy."

Grayson sat silently as the scent of the roses on Piper's grave wafted toward him. He pulled out the battered old green book. "Piper, as I'm sure you've seen, this book has transformed me, and it seems to touch everyone who comes in contact with it. After much prayer and contemplation, I've decided to start a nonprofit whose sole purpose is to get this book into as many people's hands as possible. I can't ever thank you enough for bringing it into my life."

He smiled. "Those seven steps and imitating Jesus are part of who I am now." Grayson leaned over and kissed the tombstone and whispered softly, "I love you."

As Grayson walked away, the first sentence of *The Imitation of Christ* flashed in his mind.

"'He that followeth me, walketh not in darkness,' saith the Lord. (John 8:12)" As the sun warmed his skin, he felt *the* Son whisper that truth in his soul.

Inspiration

For This Book

Bryan Taylor

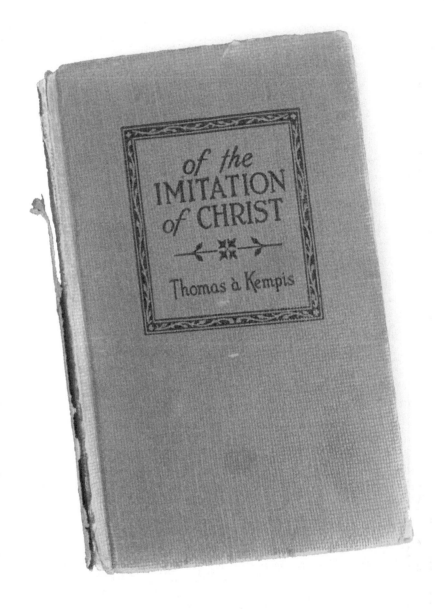

It was early April 2016 when Michael Kroth and I packed our duffel bags into the pickup and began our 6-hour drive from Caldwell, Idaho, to Mount Angel, Oregon, for our first retreat with the St. Agatha's Parish men's group. We didn't know what to expect, but both of us looked forward to a quiet, contemplative weekend at the abbey, surrounded by other brothers in Christ. Neither of us had been to Mount Angel before. Although we were different in faith backgrounds—Michael, a Methodist, and I, a Catholic—we believed this setting and experience would be inspirational for each of us in our unique ways. We did not know that a small, ragged green book would transform both of our lives and become the catalyst for the book you are holding.

Michael and I first met back in 2006. Michael was the mentor and professor, and I was the protegee and student. As I worked through my doctoral program in adult organizational leadership and learning, our relationship slowly developed into a friendship as well as an academic partnership. Upon my graduation, we continued to do research and write together.

Meanwhile, our interests gradually shifted toward contemplative and theological topics. We were talking less about adult learning theories and more about Christian mysticism, our purpose in the world, and ways to be more Christ-like in our daily encounters. Our joint interest and fervor led us to accept this men's retreat invitation from our good friend, Deacon Greg. Road trips are not as enjoyable solo, so we decided to journey together into this unexpected adventure.

Mount Angel is a Benedictine abbey and a seminary for men discerning a vocation to the priesthood. It sits atop a knoll overlooking the lush, green landscape of Oregonian farmland and forest. Anyone can easily find peace and tranquility along the walking paths. This is truly a place where angels descend.

We arrived early Friday morning to attend Mass with the seminarians. Afterwards we savored a delightful cup of coffee at the seminary bookstore. This coffee shop and bookstore inspired the setting of our tale.

As first-timers here, we were offered by a seminarian the café's specialty drink called "the Immaculate Latte," quite fitting for the location. It was quite delicious. Years later, this house special made us think that the protagonist in our book, Dr. Grayson Rogers, a man of learning, would need his own special, sophisticated cup of brew.

After our morning coffee, we headed to the Mount Angel library, an impressive and important building on campus. It is home to one of the most significant theological libraries in the Pacific Northwest. Michael and I are naturally drawn to libraries and books. We gravitated to the used books sale. With our home libraries stuffed with books, the last thing we needed was another one, but they are in our blood. While chatting in the used books section, Michael asked if I had heard of any of these books, as most seemed Catholic in nature. I eventually came across a small, worn, green book with distinctive, golden-yellow lettering: Of the Imitation of Christ. I told Michael this was an excellent book, written by Thomas à Kempis, a monk in the early 1400s. I thought Michael would like it because it captures everything he was currently reading about and might answer questions he was contemplating. I told him that I had read parts of the book many years earlier and that it had resonated with me over the years, but now it just sat on my bookcase collecting dust.

"For one dollar," Michael said, "Why not?"

The next morning, we arrived inside the church to pray lauds with the monks at 5:00 a.m. Michael looked exhausted. I eventually asked him if he had slept. He said that he couldn't put down that little green book. He explained how it had struck a chord with him and was especially meaningful to him with everything going on in his life.

What he was referring to had begun at least 6 months earlier. In October 2015, Michael's daughter, Piper, had welcomed into the world her first child, Grayson Morse. Grayson immediately brought joy to the family; however, Grayson's battle began early. After 6 months, he was diagnosed with a rare fetal disease called Krabbe disease, or globoid cell leukodystrophy. Michael's wife and daughter took Grayson across the country to Pittsburgh, Pennsylvania, where there was a new specialized treatment that might slow the disease. They had eventually stayed for 9 months, leaving Michael alone in Idaho, waiting and therefore able to make this trip with me to the abbey. So, this time at Mount Angel was a perfect setting for Michael to dive into a deeper conversation with God while he patiently waited.

After our 3-day retreat, we drove home. A month later, my wife and I, along with my daughter, Lucy, welcomed my son, Matthew Taylor, into this world. After I held him for literally 6 seconds—enough time to give him a kiss on the forehead—he was whisked away and intubated by the medical staff. My wife and I had already known that Matthew had a rare genetic birth defect called a congenital diaphragmatic hernia. He was going to have to undergo a series of surgeries over the next month to stabilize his condition. Matthew therefore spent 3 months in the neonatal intensive care unit (NICU). Most of the time he was in a contained crib, which prevented us from holding him. During this time, I came across my old copy of *The Imitation of Christ* and remembered the conversation Michael and I had at Mount Angel.

I decided that I would read the entire book during my daily visits to Matthew's bedside. It was here that I fell in love with the book. The first time I had read it, so long before, it was merely a book. Now it spoke to me.

Michael and I were experiencing challenges and sufferings in life. But we constantly saw Christ in Grayson and Matthew. Although both little guys were going through things no child should ever have to go through, we discovered how God was revealed in so many ways, through so many different people. I am afraid to say that without their suffering, we might never have embraced à Kempis's words. We found ourselves discussing *The Imitation of Christ* and how important it was to follow the guidance inside that little green book. Our lives were now ever-connected, not only through Grayson and Matthew, but also as brothers in Jesus Christ.

From there, we began the journey, which resulted in this book. We asked ourselves the question, "How do we share à Kempis's masterpiece with others?" In a world that seems to drift away from Jesus, the wisdom inside this book is sorely needed to bring people back to Him. We wondered, what format would best connect deep wisdom from a centuries-old book with people today, who likely spend a good chunk of their time looking for advice on social media?

The answer came to us: Give them a parable that is contemporaneous with today's day and age and that people can relate to. Through the grace of the Holy Spirit we partnered with Mater Media, a Catholic apostolate with the mission of "Making Jesus Christ more known, and more loved, by more people." Zip, Kari, Trese, Eric, Joey, Rachel, Cathy, Karen, and Leslie from Mater Media transformed the book into the compelling story, which you have just read.

By summarizing and examining some key messages that Thomas laid out over the four books included in *The Imitation of Christ*, we offer a modern-day portal into his most important insights about what it means, on a daily basis, to imitate Christ as best we can. This book is not meant to replace *The Imitation of Christ*. Our heartfelt desire is to complement it and to make it accessible to even more people. Everything in our book is drawn from à Kempis's magnum opus.

Our tale is simple to read, and the seven steps are logically laid out. We hope that you enjoyed this journey with Grayson and Matthew— and with a lovely young barista named Lucy. We pray that you will embrace the steps outlined and put into action the exercises provided. Ultimately, we want you to do what we all should aim to do: imitate Christ.

In the words of Thomas, "Bear the cross cheerfully and it will bear you."

In Christ's Peace,
Bryan

60 A FRA ANGELICO um 1400-1455 · DAS JÜNGSTE GERICHT

110

The Saints

of Coffee Talk

Thomas à Kempis's *The Imitation of Christ* is a mainstay of saintly life. In it, Thomas draws upon the lives of the saints that came before him, and through it, he has profoundly impacted those who came after him.

While writing this magnificent devotional, à Kempis examined the lives of saints and incorporated their teachings, writings, and actions. He refers to them throughout the book, knowing a person must follow and imitate Christ to become one.

For the saints who came after its publication, *The Imitation of Christ* provided sustenance to a thirsty spiritual life. It helped instill faith and provide direction as the spiritual lessons contained within the pages propelled them to new heights of sanctity.

This classic has been purchased by untold millions through the centuries and has transformed countless lives. In *Coffee Talk,* we demonstrated the conversional power of this masterpiece and mentioned several saints that the book has inspired.

The story did not allow for a thorough discussion of these extraordinary men and women, so we decided to place that information here. Their lives should be constant reminders that all can become saints by following Christ and striving to be holy. Let's listen to the call of our Savior, follow the saints who have gone before us, and live out our lives imitating Christ!

St. Ignatius of Loyola

Date of life: 1491 – 1556 AD

Location: Spain

Step: Examination of Conscience

His connection to the Imitation of Christ

St. Ignatius of Loyola was so fond of *The Imitation of Christ* that it is said to have been one of the only two books in his room at the time of his death – along with the Gospels of the New Testament. *The Imitation of Christ* was a transformational book in his life.

Life of St. Ignatius of Loyola

Ignatius was born in the castle at Loyola in 1491 A.D. He was far from saintly during his young adult life. Vanity and pride flowed through him resulting in bountiful aspirations of fame and honor. He was a womanizer, a gambler, a swordsman who was sensitive to insult, and he engaged in a plethora of sinful activities. He is one of the only saints to have an actual police record from participating in a nighttime brawl.

Ignatius's derelict life changed suddenly in the spring of 1521. He was 30 years old, and an officer in the Spanish army, when he was thrust into a battle at Pamplona. Frenchmen had attacked the town and Ignatius led a rag-tag group of soldiers on defense. Although his men were less than gallant,

Ignatius fought valiantly until he was struck in the leg by a cannonball. The enemies admired his courage so much that they carried him back to his castle in Loyola.

Although his life was spared, in Ignatius's eyes it was destroyed with the blast of the cannon. His aspirations, ambitions, and dreams were shattered along with his leg. The doctors did such a poor job resetting the bones that they protruded hideously for the rest of his life, cutting straight to the core of his vanity. Ultimately, his leg healed shorter than the other and he limped for the rest of his life.

During Ignatius's difficult recovery, while he lay in bed immobilized, he asked if there were any romantic chivalry books lying around. He was told there were none and was instead given Vita Christi (The Life of Christ) and a book about the lives of the saints. As Ignatius studied them his life was transformed, and he committed to follow and imitate Christ.

Shortly after he recovered enough to begin walking again, he was introduced to Thomas à Kempis's *The Imitation of Christ*. Ignatius referred to this book as the "partridge," the savoriest of all spiritual books, and recommended it to everyone. It is said that Ignatius would open The Imitation at random times and always come across a much-needed passage for that moment.

Ignatius ended up embarking on his own pilgrimage, trying to imitate Christ. When he traveled through the town of Montserrat, near Barcelona, Spain, he gave away his fine clothing to a poor man. Then, during an all-night vigil before the Black Madonna, he hung up his sword and dagger. At that point, he completely gave up his old life and embraced his new one.

Although St. Ignatius was challenged with intellectual questions and difficult dilemmas, he never stopped examining his conscience and focusing on Christ. He is best known for his spiritual exercises and the simple practice of examining one's conscience. Much of what Ignatius developed stemmed from learning to better imitate Christ.

Thomas's little book became the centerpiece for one of the great saints of the last five hundred years. It is likely that Ignatius reflected on its numerous quotes, such as this one:

> Examine your conscience carefully and, to the best of your ability, cleanse and purify it by sincere contrition and a humble confession, so that you may not be aware of anything to fill you with remorse, or prevent your free approach to God. (Bk. 4, Ch. 7)

Prayer for Conscience Formation by St. Ignatius

I praise you Lord for creating me in your divine image. Thank you for giving me a free will to know you and love you. Open my heart to your teachings and help me to form my conscience according to your will. Please strengthen me with the virtues of faith, hope, love, and especially prudence. Grant me your loving guidance each day and send me the graces to always do your will, even when most difficult.

Amen

Recommended reading: *The Spiritual Exercises* by St. Ignatius of Loyola

St. Philip Neri

His connection to the Imitation of Christ

St. Philip Neri was a mystic, a missionary, and a big fan of *The Imitation of Christ*. It helped guide him in humility, and he claimed it was a book that should not be read indiscriminately.

Life of St. Philip Neri

St. Philip Neri grew up in Florence, Italy in the early 1500s. He was known for his cheerfulness and obedience. At around 18 years of age, Philip experienced a mystical vision that triggered his conversion to the Christian faith. Led by the Holy Spirit, he transformed his life and began to serve Jesus.

Philip left his home in Florence and moved to Rome, where he studied theology and philosophy, while focusing on helping the poor. Because he had a passion for evangelization and could jovially start up a conversation with anyone, he began a ministry of talking to people throughout the city with gaiety, friendship, and playful wit.

Philip imitated Christ, cultivated virtues in his daily life, and practiced prudence while navigating decades of conflicts in the

Church. He exhibited temperance by famously leading walks to seven churches in Rome. At each church he would lead prayer, songs, and a reflection - a stark contrast to the often out-of-control Roman festivals of the time. The walks weren't boring, pious trudges; they always featured food, music, and merriment.

Before long, Philip became known as the "Apostle of Joy," because in addition to being holy he was witty, funny, and fun. He showed the people of Rome that they did not have to be melancholy to achieve holiness. He used to say, "A joyful heart is more easily made perfect than a downcast one."

Eventually, he was ordained a priest. Because he had quite the following, a large room was built above a church to tend to Philip's growing number of pilgrims. The priests who assisted him were called the Oratorians, which later became the religious order entitled Congregation of the Priests of the Oratory.

To Philip, humility was the most important virtue. His approach to teaching humility was unique, and oftentimes laced with humor. One time, after a priest gave a beautiful sermon, Philip ordered him to give it six times in a row so people would think he only had one sermon. Although at times the lessons seemed cruel, they seemed to be tailored to what the person needed.

Philip also had a gift for penetrating the interior of one's heart. One time Pope Gregory XIII sent him to investigate a young nun who claimed to be imitating Christ as a living saint in private communication with God. Philip traveled to her small village through a violent storm. When he arrived at the convent soaking wet in mud-covered boots, the sisters greeted him and invited him in. Philip sat down in a chair and asked the young nun if she would mind taking off his boots and fixing him a drink, as the journey had been long. The young nun basically told him, "No thank you, you can do it yourself." Philip immediately got up, walked out, and left. When he arrived back in Rome, he told Pope Gregory that the young nun was not authentic and not in communication with God. Pope Gregory inquired as to how Philip knew this if he did not converse with her. Philip told the pope that if she truly were imitating Christ and in communication with God, she would have practiced humility and taken off his boots.

Philip was completely devoted to imitating Christ. Through humility, he brought himself below all those he encountered. He believed that a priest must be Christlike. To draw others to Jesus, one must lead their life by joy, fervor, pastoral solicitude, and the wide array of virtues. He believed imitation leads to imitation. He was correct!

> **Many seek to fly [from] temptations, and fall more grievously into them. By flight alone we cannot overcome; but by patience and true humility we are made stronger than our enemies. He who only declines them outwardly, and does not pluck out the root, will profit little; nay, temptations will sooner return to him, and he will find himself in a worse condition. By degrees, and by patience . . . thou shalt by God's grace better overcome them than by harshness and thine own importunity [or anxieties] (Bk. 1, Ch. 13).**

Prayer to St. Philip Neri

Saint Philip Neri, we take ourselves far too seriously most of the time. Help us to add humor to our perspective - remembering always that humor is a gift from God.

Amen.

Recommended Reading: *The Life of St. Philip Neri* by Fr. Pietro Bacci

St. Thomas More

Date of Life: 1478 – 1535 AD

Location: England

Step: Avoiding Temptation

His connection to the Imitation of Christ

St. Thomas More admired *The Imitation of Christ* and followed its instruction as it guided his life. At a time when few people owned books, and even fewer owned more than one book, he believed *The Imitation of Christ* should be owned by everyone.

Life of St. Thomas More

St. Thomas More lived at the end of the 1400s and beginning of the 1500s, which was the start of Henry VIII's reign. After an exceedingly privileged upbringing, which included attending the finest schools and universities in England, he became a lawyer. Although he was quite successful in his practice, he felt as though he was being guided down a different path. Thomas lived next to a Carthusian monastery and found himself called to follow the lifestyle of simple piety, even though he never joined.

Ultimately, More was elected to the English Parliament. As he continued to ascend in the world of politics, Henry VIII took a liking to him. Henry gave Thomas posts with increasing responsibility, culminating with the lord chancellor, the second most powerful position in the country. In that role, Thomas was responsible for overseeing all the courts and judiciary in England.

During that era, lord chancellors were typically religious men who were given the responsibility to keep the faith intact. Thomas was extremely effective and followed the law as it was laid out. During his time as lord chancellor, he prosecuted individuals who were accused of heresy and worked tirelessly to defend the Catholic faith in England.

Unfortunately for Thomas More, Henry decided he wanted a divorce from his wife, Catherine of Aragon, to marry Anne Boleyn, with whom he hoped to have a male heir. He needed to obtain an annulment, and it was at this time that Thomas's temptations and tribulations began.

Thomas refused to sign a letter to the pope requesting the annulment, because he did not find proper grounds for granting it. Despite their long friendship, Henry grew increasingly hostile with Thomas, eventually having charges brought up against him. The king ordered Thomas to take an oath acknowledging the legitimacy of Anne Boleyn's position as queen and elevating his kingship to include head of the Church in England.

More had a choice: Take the oath or be executed. Temptation was presented as a binary decision—to live by betraying his integrity, or to die with his integrity intact.

Imitating Jesus, More chose the path of integrity, and like Jesus, he died as a result. Because he refused to acknowledge the King's demands, More was locked away in the Tower of London and put on trial, where he was convicted in 15 minutes. As punishment, he was beheaded. In his final statement before kneeling for the executioner's blow, he said, "I die the king's good servant, but God's first."

St. Thomas More, the mighty lord chancellor, could have lived in luxury to the end of his days, but chose to follow Christ instead. Thomas had prepared for this moment over a lifetime.

He knew what it meant to imitate Christ. He was a man of deep piety, asceticism, voluntary self-discipline, and penitence - all of which are ways to imitate Christ. After his death, it was discovered that Thomas wore a hair shirt. Hair shirts were intended to be uncomfortable and were worn as a sign of continual repentance and a constant reminder of temptations. It is likely that Thomas was familiar with this passage of *The Imitation of Christ*:

> **We will never be free of trials and temptations as long as our earthly life lasts... Is not the life of human beings on earth a drudgery? Therefore, we should always be on our guard against temptations, always praying that our enemy, the devil, "who never sleeps but constantly looks for someone to devour," (1 Pet 5:8)... No one in this world is so perfect or holy as not to have temptations sometimes. We can never be entirely free from them. Sometimes these temptations can be very severe and trou-**

blesome, but if we resist them, they will be very useful to us; for by experiencing them we are humbled, cleansed, and instructed. All the Saints endured tribulations and temptations and profited by them, while those who did not resist and overcome them fell away and were lost. There is no place so holy or remote where you will not meet with temptation, nor is there anyone completely free from it in this life; for in our body we bear the wounds of sin—the weakness of our human nature in which we are born" (Bk. 1, Ch. 13).

Prayer for Resistance to Temptation by St. Thomas More

Almighty God, who of your infinite goodness did create our first parents in the state of innocence, with present wealth and hope of heaven to come till through the devil's deceit their folly fell by sin to wretchedness: by Your tender pity of that Passion that was paid for their and our redemption, assist me with Your gracious help so that to the subtle suggestions of the serpent I never so incline the ears of my heart but that my reason may resist them and master my sensuality and keep me from them.

Amen.

Recommended Reading: *The Complete Works of St. Thomas More* by St. Thomas More

St. Anthony the Great

Date of Life: 251 – 356 A.D.

Location: Egypt

Step: Prayer

His connection to the Imitation of Christ

St. Anthony the Great, also known as St. Anthony of the Desert or St. Anthony of Egypt, was one of the early saints who provided inspiration to *The Imitation of Christ*. Thomas á Kempis likely relied on St. Anthony's example, showing why it is important to have a strong prayer life.

Life of St. Anthony the Great

Anthony was born in Egypt in the mid-third century. He came from a good Christian family who possessed considerable wealth. Unfortunately, his parents passed away when he was around 20 years old, leaving Anthony at a crossroad in his life. He prayed intently, looking for what God wanted him to do and wondering how he could walk like the Apostles.

Anthony was asking God to reveal his purpose. How does one truly follow Jesus Christ and imitate Him? At a Sunday Mass, Anthony heard a reading from Matthew's Gospel about Jesus and the rich young man. Jesus told the wealthy man what he needed to do to follow Him and enjoy eternal salvation. "If you wish to be perfect, go, sell what you have and give to the poor, and you will have treasure in heaven. Then come, follow me" (Matthew 19:21). Those words struck him deeply and he took it as an answer to his prayer. Wanting to follow the Lord, he sold all his possessions and donated the proceeds to the villagers.

Anthony began to live a life of prayer, work, solitude, and learning. He met with very holy persons asking questions, gaining insight, and soaking in their wisdom. He absorbed what he heard, began to read Scripture, and started praying throughout the day.

It was prayer that helped Anthony resist and endure terrible temptations from the devil. The devil will do everything he can to lead people away from Jesus, and Anthony was no exception. The devil tried to tempt him with wealth by reminding him of the posh lifestyle he had before he gave it all away. When that did not work, he tried to tempt him with boredom and laziness. Anthony countered every temptation with prayer and grew in holiness.

Anthony moved to an unused tomb in a graveyard which allowed him to drift more toward a life of solitude, prayer, and friendship with Christ. This just escalated the devil's anger. One night the devil sent demons to beat up Anthony. While being pummeled, Anthony cried out in prayer telling the demons there was no level of pain that would separate him from the love of Christ. Anthony was beaten to unconsciousness. Fortunately, Anthony's friends found his brutally beaten body and took him to a local church. As Anthony's wounds healed, he asked in prayer to God, "Where have You been, O Merciful Jesus? Why didn't You appear from the very beginning to end my pain?" The Lord replied, "I was here, Anthony, but wanted to see your struggle and fight. Now, since you have not yielded, I shall always help you and make your name known throughout the entire world." Having heard this, Anthony became stronger both spiritually and physically.

He recognized that a deep devotional way of life does not happen overnight. It takes time, practice, and faith. After that experience with the devil, Anthony moved into the desert where he could devote himself completely to prayer and penance. For twenty years, he lived in complete isolation without seeing another person's face. Only after two decades did he invite monks to live with him.   Anthony's devout prayer life, holiness, and constant battles with the devil garnered great attention, including people seeking spiritual direction and assistance. One time a military officer brought his daughter, afflicted with an evil spirit. The officer asked Anthony to rid her of the demon. Anthony chastised the father, asking why he would come to him, a mere man, rather than praying to Jesus. He instructed the father to pray to God, and told him if he believed, the evil spirit would leave his daughter. The man prayed to Jesus and the evil spirit left.

Anthony healed not by commanding, but by prayer and speaking the name of Christ. His advice to his monks went something like, "Believe in God. Love Him. Pray continually. Avoid vainglory. Sing the Psalms before you sleep and when you wake up. Follow the commandments in Scripture. Be mindful of the works of the saints and follow in their footsteps."

Anthony lived only on bread and water, and eventually died at the ripe old age of 105. Many believe it was his spiritual food (his prayer life) that truly sustained him for over a century.

Anthony completely dedicated his life to Jesus. It was prayer that comforted him through the temptations and allowed him to grow in holiness. His story shows that prayer is critical to the Christian life and must be central if one genuinely wants to imitate Christ.

The story of St. Anthony does not suggest that one needs to live as a hermit, but it demonstrates why prayer is so important. When Anthony prayed, he knew Jesus was there with him through everything. He truly had faith. What moved him the most in his prayer life was that he trusted Jesus. Jesus guided him, strengthened him, and alleviated his suffering. Even the simplest of prayers brought Anthony closer to Jesus. Merely meditating, and opening his heart and mind, became a spiritually-enriching practice. He imitated Christ by having a devout prayer life and his deep trust in God, and in God's love for him, was at the root of it all.

Thomas à Kempis might have drawn upon St. Anthony the Great when he wrote the following passage in *The Imitation of Christ*:

> **Convert thyself with thy whole heart to the Lord, and quit this miserable world, and thy soul shall find rest. Learn to despise exterior things, and give thyself to the interior, and thou shalt see the Kingdom of God will come into thee. For the Kingdom of God is peace and joy in the Holy Ghost, which is not given to the wicked (Bk. 2, Ch. 1).**

The Miracle Prayer to St. Anthony the Great

O Holy St. Anthony, gentlest of Saints, your love for God and charity for His creatures made you worthy, when on earth, to possess miraculous powers. Encouraged by this thought, I implore you to obtain for me (request).

O gentle and loving St. Anthony, whose heart was ever full of human sympathy, whisper my petition into the ears of the sweet Infant Jesus, who loved to be folded in your arms. The gratitude of my heart will ever be yours. Amen.

Recommended Reading: *Life of St. Antony* by St. Athanasius

St. Alphonsus Liguori

Date of Life:1696 – 1787 AD

Location: Italy

Step: Embracing the Sacraments

His Connection to the Imitation of Christ

St. Alphonsus Liguori is a Doctor of the Catholic Church, a mighty moral theologian. Alphonsus's entire life centered on imitating Christ. He called *The Imitation of Christ* a 'golden little book,' and relied heavily on the work of à Kempis in his own spiritual writings. His life is an example for the everyday Christian who has difficulty recognizing the dignity of living a proper Christian life. He embraced à Kempis's book — a model of how to live a proper life amid the never-ending problems, pains, and failures that impede our daily lives.

Life of St. Alphonsus Liguori

St. Alphonsus Liguori was born in the late 1600s near Naples, Italy. He obtained his doctorate by the age of 16, and then started his early career as a lawyer.

Once, when he had lost an important case and was trying to figure out life, he visited a hospital to pray for the sick who were incurable. There he heard an inner voice that said, "Leave the world and give yourself to me." So he went to the local oratory, gave up his legal career, and started his new vocational call to priesthood.

As a young priest he cared for the poor and worked himself to the point of exhaustion. He adopted a style of ministry to "mission among the people," and he began the Congregation of the Most Holy Redeemer, a religious community now commonly known as the Redemptorists. He was a brilliant, articulate, and pragmatic preacher, and his teachings resonated with people.

Central to Alphonsus' preaching and teaching were three powerful images: Jesus as an infant in the crib, Jesus crucified on the Cross, and Jesus vibrantly alive and filled with love for all in the Eucharist. Jesus was central to Alphonsus, and so was *The Imitation of Christ*.

Alphonsus wrote more than a hundred books, many of which quote à Kempis's classic. One of his more famous works is titled, Visits to the Blessed Sacrament. In that book, Alphonsus makes it clear that among all devotions, adoring Jesus in the Blessed Sacrament holds first place after receiving the sacraments themselves. Eucharistic adoration is the devotion most pleasing to God and the most useful to ourselves.

We must approach Jesus to converse with Him in the Blessed Sacrament, without fear of chastisement nor restraint, as we would converse with a beloved friend. He quoted à Kempis:

> You alone speak to me, and I to you; as the beloved is wont to speak to his beloved, and a friend to entertain himself with his friend (Bk. 4, Ch. 13, referring to Exodus 33:11).

Alphonsus believed that of all the gifts God has given the Church, the greatest is the Blessed Sacrament. It is the Body, Blood, Soul and Divinity of Jesus Christ. There is no better way to imitate Christ than to be in His presence. Alphonsus believed that when you reflect before the Blessed Eucharist you will truly discover Him.

St. Alphonsus Liguori captures it quite nicely, by writing something four hundred years ago that remains true today: "Adoring Jesus in the Blessed Sacrament is the greatest of all devotions. Because this devotion is the dearest to God and is the most helpful to us."

Prayer of St. Alphonsus Liguori before the Eucharist
(From Visits to the Blessed Sacrament, published in 1745)

My LORD Jesus Christ, who because of Your love for men remain night and day in the Blessed Sacrament, full of pity and of love, awaiting, calling and welcoming all who come to visit You, I believe that You are present here on the altar. I adore You, and I thank You for all the graces You have bestowed on me, especially for having given me Yourself in this Sacrament, for having given me Your most holy Mother Mary to plead for me, and for having called me to visit You in this church.

I now salute Your most loving Heart, and that for three ends: first, in thanksgiving for this great gift; secondly, to make amends to You for all the outrages committed against You in this Sacrament by Your enemies; thirdly, I intend by this visit to adore You in all the places on earth in which You are present in the Blessed Sacrament and in which You are least honored and most abandoned.

My Jesus, I love You with my whole heart. I am very sorry for having so many times offended Your infinite goodness. With the help of Your grace, I purpose never to offend You again. And now, unworthy though I am, I consecrate myself to You without reserve. I renounce and give entirely to You my will, my affection, my desires and all that I possess. For the future, dispose of me and all I have as You please.

All I ask of You is Your holy love, final perseverance and that I may carry out Your will perfectly. I recommend to You the souls in Purgatory, especially those who had the greatest devotion to the Blessed Sacrament and to the Blessed Virgin Mary. I also recommend to You all poor sinners.

Finally, my dear Savior, I unite all my desires with the desires of Your most loving Heart; and I offer them, thus united, to the Eternal Father, and beseech Him, in Your name and for love of You, to accept and grant them.

Recommend Reading: *Visits to the Most Holy Eucharist* by St. Alphonsus Liguori

St. Lucy of Syracuse

Date of Life: 283 – 304 A.D.

Location: Syracuse, Roman Empire (island of Sicily)

Step: Working of the Holy Spirit

Her connection to the Imitation of Christ

St. Lucy was one of the early saints that likely influenced Thomas á Kempis. She immersed herself in the Holy Spirit as she suffered martyrdom for Jesus Christ. Like other early martyrs, she imitated Christ and sacrificed her life for her love for Jesus.

Life of St. Lucy of Syracuse

St. Lucy lived in Sicily, an island off the coast of Italy. As a young girl she vowed to live her life in the service of Christ. When she was still very young, her father died and left behind a huge dowry to give to whomever was to marry her.

Her mother, who had a severe bleeding illness, wanted her daughter to get married before she passed away. She tried to arrange a marriage between Lucy and a rich pagan man, believing that he would take care of her. Lucy did not want to marry him, but instead wanted to distribute her dowry to the poor.

At that time in the Roman Empire, Christianity was an illegal religion. Practicing Christians were often arrested and executed. As a teenager, Lucy had helped fellow Christians avoid the persecutions of the Roman emperor Diocletian and hid them in catacombs. She wore a wreath of candles on her head to find her way in the dark, because her hands were full of food and drink for the people.

Lucy did not want to give up her service to the poor, nor did she want to marry this pagan man. One day, Lucy and her mother went to the tomb of St. Agatha and after several prayers they fell asleep. While they slept, St. Agatha came to Lucy in a dream and told her that her mother's illness would be cured because of Lucy's faith. Upon waking, Lucy conveyed the dream to her mother—and lo and behold, her mother's illness was cured! Both Lucy and her mother were grateful to God, and her mother clearly saw that Lucy should have Christ as her only partner in life.

When the bridegroom heard the news he was furious, mostly because he lost out on the huge dowry. He was so angry he decided to destroy Lucy's life by denouncing her as a Christian to the governor of the province.

The governor, wanting to teach Lucy a lesson and make an example out of her, planned to place her at a local brothel to destroy her commitment to Christ as a consecrated virgin. The soldiers arrived at her home and tried to seize her; however, Lucy, filled with the Holy Spirit, could not physically be moved. Next the soldiers hitched her to a team of oxen, but the oxen were unable to move her. When the governor heard that Lucy could not be moved, he asked her how she could be so strong. She said it was through the power of the Holy Spirit because she was the bridesmaid of Jesus Christ, her Lord. Lucy warned the governor that he would be punished if he continued to persecute her and other Christians.

The governor decided to have her killed and wanted her eyes gouged out, at the request of the pagan man who was supposed to marry her. Lucy was well known for her beautiful eyes; it was said they radiated her love for Christ.

The guards first decided to burn her inside her house. They placed bundles of wood around her and attempted to light her on fire, but they were unable to light it. Frustrated and angry, they decided to kill her by taking up their swords, and Lucy did finally meet her death in this way. The guards cut out her eyes, as ordered, and placed them on a platter for the governor. When Lucy's body was being readied for burial, those preparing her discovered that her eyes had been restored!

St. Lucy was a virgin and martyr of the early Church. She was a brave young woman who zealously gave her life to God. With the Holy Spirit she was unmovable. In her own words, "Those whose hearts are pure are the temples of the Holy Spirit."

When Thomas á Kempis wrote about the importance of being immersed in the Holy Spirit, he was possibly thinking of saints such as St. Lucy. The following passage captures her well:

> The doctrine of Christ exceeds all the doctrines of holy men [and women]; and he that has the Spirit, will find therein a hidden manna. But it happens that many who often hear the Gospel of Christ, are yet but little affected, because they are void of the Spirit of Christ. But whoever would fully and feelingly understand the words of Christ, must endeavor to conform his life wholly to the life of Christ (Bk. 1, Ch. 1).

Saint Lucy's Prayer

Saint Lucy, you did not hide your light under a basket, but let it shine for the whole world, for all the centuries to see. We may not suffer torture in our lives the way you did, but we are still called to let the light of our Christianity illumine our daily lives. Please help us to have the courage to bring our Christianity into our work, our recreation, our relationships, our conversation -- every corner of our day.

Amen

Recommended Reading: *The Life and Prayers of St. Lucy of Syracuse* by Wyatt North.

St. Thérèse of Lisieux

Date of Life: 1873 – 1897 AD

Location: France

Step: Imitating Christ

Her connection to the Imitation of Christ

St. Thérèse of Lisieux was known as "The Little Flower." *The Imitation of Christ* had a profound influence on her spirituality. Thérèse was extremely attached to à Kempis's book and read it so frequently she could quote passages from memory. She herself wrote, "For a long time I had nourished my spiritual life with the 'fine flour' contained in *The Imitation of Christ*. It was the only book which did me good, for I had not yet found the treasures hidden in the Holy Gospels. I always had it with me, to the amusement of my people at home." She used the book in her daily prayer life and distilled its messages to examine them in her writings. Her own work went on to greatly influence Christian spirituality.

Life of St. Thérèse of Lisieux

St. Thérèse grew up in France in the late 1800s. She was a meek, weak, young girl, who was plagued by illness most of her life. She originated what is known as the 'Little Way' — an approach to serving God through one's littleness with simplicity and love. She was not rich, famous, or capable of making great sacrifices or performing glorious works. Rather, Thérèse chose to remain a child in the eyes of God, and she performed all her duties with love and obedience no matter how small they were. Even though she died of tuberculosis at the youthful age of 24, she was proclaimed a Doctor, or great thinker, of the Catholic Church for her simple approach in imitating Jesus.

Thérèse is the perfect model for imitating Christ. She dedicated her entire life to prayer, suffering, and the self-emptying love of God. In her religious community, there was an aridity and dryness to her daily activities. She would go through the motions of normal tasks and duties, but unlike most, she embraced them.

What moved her was her desire to imitate Christ. She often turned to Scripture and read the Gospel stories of Jesus. She found that the simplest prayers and miniscule actions brought her closer to God. Merely meditating and opening her heart and mind when doing something as simple as cleaning, became a spiritually enriching practice as she began to imitate Christ. Her deep trust in God and in God's love for her was at the root of it all. It was her simplicity that made her great. She recognized that you do not need to change the world to follow Christ.

Sometimes people try too hard, missing that the simple things are the most important. Totally trusting in God as our loving Father and seeking to imitate Christ in everyday activities is foundational. When one does everything for the love of Jesus through humility, they are imitating Him. Love is an excellent thing, and in loving one another you in turn love Jesus. Thérèse could quote this passage from memory:

Love makes light of all that is burdensome and equally bears all that is unequal. Love carries a burden without being burdened and makes all that which is bitter, sweet and savory. Love of Jesus spurs us on to do great things and excites us to desire always that which is most perfect (Bk. 3, Ch. 5).

Little prayer composed by St. Thérèse of Lisieux

O Little Infant Jesus, my only treasure, I abandon myself to Your every wish. I seek no other joy than that of calling forth Your sweet smile. Grant me the graces and the virtues of Your Holy Childhood, so that on the day of my birth into Heaven the angels and saints may recognize me as Your little spouse.

Amen.

Recommend Reading: *Story of a Soul* by St. Thérèse of Lisieux

St. Augustine

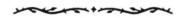

Date of Life: 354 – 430 A.D.

Location: Hippo, Northern Africa

Step: Every Step

His connection to the Imitation of Christ

St. Augustine is one of the foundational pillars of the Catholic Church and one of its early great Doctors. He is the only saint whom á Kempis references in *The Imitation of Christ*, and he relied heavily on St. Augustine's life, teaching, and writings while composing it. Augustinian principles are scattered throughout the book.

Life of St. Augustine

St. Augustine's life is one that is very well known, primarily because of his autobiography, Confessions. Augustine was born in northern Africa in 354 A.D. Augustine's mother, St. Monica, was a devout Christian who tried her best to raise Augustine in the Catholic faith. Augustine was a difficult child and more interested in sex and high-living than in religion and God. His sins of impurity and pride darkened his mind so much that he cast God aside and grew to be an atheist. He eventually moved away from home, when he was 17 years old, to Carthage where he studied philosophy and succumbed to the heresy of Manichaeism. During this time, Augustine set up a household with a concubine whom he deeply loved and with whom he had a son.

Shortly after, he took a position as a professor in Rome. He continued to lead a dissolute life of debauchery. A year later, he took a position as public orator in the City of Milan. There he met the bishop, St. Ambrose, who was a convincing theologian, orator, and defender of the Catholic faith. Augustine was constantly searching for the truth, and because St. Ambrose taught only that, he was instrumental in Augustine's conversion.

The decisive moment when Augustine changed his life for good took place one day in a garden. While Augustine was sitting, he heard a child singing, "Take up and read! Take up and read!" Feeling a divine nudge, Augustine picked up a collection of St. Paul's epistles. He read a passage in Romans (13:13-14), an exhortation to abandon licentiousness and follow Christ. At this moment, Augustine was confronted with his sinful life and need for redemption. He knew he needed to put away all impurity and follow Jesus. Augustine remarked that after reading the passage he had no desire nor need to read further. In the instant that sentence ended, it was as if a peaceful light shone in his heart and all the darkness of doubt vanished. At that moment, he embraced Christian life and began to imitate Christ.

Augustine resigned his professorship, told St. Ambrose of this conversion, and retreated off to a country villa, eventually ending back in Africa in the city of Hippo. In quick time, Augustine was baptized, became a priest, and against his desires, was elected bishop of Hippo.

Augustine became a pillar in the early Catholic Church, a prolific writer, and a defender of the faith. Augustine wrote one of the greatest sentences ever written. It can be found in Confessions, and was so profound that it was incorporated into *The Imitation of Christ*:

> **You have made us for yourself, and our hearts are restless until they rest in you (Bk. 3, Ch. 21).**

Imitating Christ is about life itself because God has made us for Himself. Our hearts yearn for Him and are restless until we are with Him. Our hearts find joy in praising God and imitating His Son. Otherwise, restlessness will consume one's existence. Jesus Christ shows us the way to God. Christ reveals God to man and man to himself by being both perfectly God and perfectly man. Therefore, imitating Jesus Christ is the perfect way for us to become saints and enter heaven.

Prayer of St. Augustine

Lord Jesus, let me know myself and know you,

And desire nothing, save only you.

Let me hate myself and love you.

Let me do everything for the sake of you.

Let me humble myself and exalt you.

Let me think of nothing except you.

Let me accept whatever happens as from you.

Let me banish self and follow you,

And ever desire to follow you.

Let me fly from myself and take refuge in you,

That I may deserve to be defended by you.

Let me fear for myself, let me fear you,

And let me be among those who are chosen by you.

Let me be willing to obey for the sake of you.

Let me cling to nothing, save only to you,

And let me be poor because of you.

Look upon me, that I may love you.

Call me, that I may see you,

And forever enjoy you. Amen

Recommended Readings: *The Confessions* by St. Augustine of Hippo

St. Dominic Savio

Date of Life: 1842 – 1857 A.D.

Location: Italy

His connection to the Imitation of Christ

St. Dominic Savio's favorite spiritual book was *The Imitation of Christ*. He embraced its words and cultivated the virtues. He imitated Christ beautifully by living a simplified life and performing his everyday duties in an extraordinary way.

Life of St. Dominic Savio

St. Dominic Savio was born in the mid-1800s in a small town in northern Italy to a wonderful Christian family that was not wealthy. By the age of 4, he was already praying by himself and was frequently found in solitude, examining his conscience, and praying. He was allowed to receive his First Holy Communion at the age of 7. In those days, first communion was normally received around the age of 12, but because Dominic was catechized well and deeply understood the Eucharist, his priest made an exception. St. Dominic said the day he received his First Communion was the happiest and most wonderful day of his life. Even as a little boy he showed virtue and embraced the teachings in *The Imitation of Christ*.

One day at school, a classmate who had a history of misbehavior committed a serious offense, and Dominic was falsely accused. The teacher threatened to expel him, but because Dominic had never been in trouble before, gave him a severe scolding in front of the entire class. In true Christian fashion, Dominic made no reply but stood in silence with his head bowed. A few days later, the teacher discovered who the true culprit was. Feeling badly about his harsh words to Dominic, the teacher asked why he had not defended himself. Dominic responded, "I knew that the other boy was in trouble for other things. I remember how Our Lord had been unjustly accused, and I hoped that if I kept silent, he would be given another chance." This response came from an 11-year-old!

The teacher, recognizing the holiness of young Dominic, told him that he should meet John Bosco. Father Bosco, who also became a saint, was one of the heads of an oratory in Turin, Italy. He provided poor boys with lodging, food, and shelter in exchange for assisting him with apostolic work. When they met, Dominic told Father Bosco that he was ready to become a priest and wanted to travel with him to begin his studies.

Father Bosco was uncertain about bringing this young fellow with him. He gave Dominic a copy of The Catholic Readings, a short pamphlet dealing with Catholic apologetics, and told him if he could recite and explain the meaning of the material the following day, he could come to Turin. Dominic read the whole thing in just a few minutes and was able to recite and explain every point.

From that moment on, his spiritual life blossomed under the guidance of Father Bosco. Just 6 months after Dominic arrived at the Turin oratory, he gave a talk on sainthood, centering on three points. First, it is God's will that each person should become a saint. Second, it is easy to become a saint. Third, a great reward waits in Heaven for those who try to become saints.

Dominic was so committed that he tried to perform physical penances and bodily mortifications, such as sleeping with a thin cover in winter, wearing a hair shirt, and eating only bread and water. When Father Bosco heard of his self-punishment, he forbade Dominic from continuing with these practices because he was concerned they would affect his health.

He told Dominic the best penance he could do was to cultivate the virtues and perform all his regular duties with perfection and humility, recalling that obedience is a greater sacrifice than any bodily mortification. This admonition formed an important aspect of Dominic's spiritual life. He recognized that he could not do big things, but he could do everything for the glory of God. From that time on, Dominic never complained about food, the weather, or his peers. He embraced every aspect of suffering cheerfully, and imitated Christ's example beautifully.

Dominic incorporated the steps and guidance of *The Imitation of Christ* into his daily life. His mother remarked that he slipped out of the playground every day to visit the Blessed Sacrament, and she often saw him at prayer, staying behind in the church after others had left. "When he is in church," she said, "he is like an angel living in paradise."

Dominic constantly observed the temptations surrounding him and relied heavily on his two beloved friends: Mary and Jesus. One time, Father Bosco found him in the sanctuary, engaged in a conversation with what appeared to be an invisible person. He heard Dominic say, "Yes, Lord, I have said it before, and I will keep on saying it: I love you and I want to love you all my life. If you see that I am about to commit a sin, make me die first! Yes, death first, but not sin!" John Bosco was so impressed by the continual piousness, progression of virtue, and saintliness in Dominic that he began to write down everything he noticed. His notes eventually become his biography of St. Dominic Savio.

Dominic had a devotion to *The Imitation of Christ* and followed its teachings each day. Dominic knew the words of God must be heard with humility; he must have reflected on this passage of *The Imitation of Christ*:

My words are spirit and life, and not to be estimated by the sense of man (Bk. 3, Ch. 3, referring to John 6:69).

A Prayer to St. Dominic Savio

Glorious St. Dominic Savio, who, burning with the desire of increasing the glory of God and of His Spouse the Church, invariably attended to the sanctification of your own soul and the edification of others, by the constant practice of prayer and charity, penance, and all Christian virtues; so that, becoming in the Church a model of holiness, you are now in heaven the protector of all those who have recourse to you in faith: cast a benign eye upon us who invoke your powerful patronage. Increase in us that true piety which forms the characteristic of the sons of God. Cause us, in imitation of you, to have, like faithful servants, our loins girt, and our lamps burning in our hands, and to live in edifying penitence; that when the eternal Master comes we may be found ready to depart from this exile, and merit to be admitted to those eternal tabernacles, where we shall see what we now believe, and obtain what now we hope for, the enjoyment of the immortal King of ages, to Whom be honor, glory, and benediction given, forever and ever. Amen.

Recommended Reading: *The Life of Dominic Savio* by St. John Bosco

About
the Authors

Bryan Taylor

Bryan Taylor was born in Kuna, Idaho and grew up on the family farm. He earned a BA in political science at Boise State University and a JD at the University of Denver.

After prosecuting cases in Idaho, Bryan moved to Eastern Europe where he taught law in Belarus, Ukraine, and Moldova. He has worked with legal experts and law faculty for over a decade in the Republic of Tajikistan and has trained prosecutors and judges in Moldova, Egypt, and Lebanon.

In 2004, he returned to Idaho as a prosecutor. He has served as the elected prosecuting attorney for Canyon County, Idaho since 2010.

Over the last 2 decades, Bryan has taught thousands of law enforcement professionals, prosecutors, judges, victim coordinators, laws professors, and students on a plethora of topics, and has shared his expertise as a specialist for the American Bar Association's Rule of Law Initiative.

While completing a doctorate in Adult, Organization Learning and Leadership at the University of Idaho, he met Michael Kroth.

Having an MA in theology from the Notre Dame Graduate School at Christendom College, he is pursuing a licentiate in canon law from St. Paul's University in Ottawa, Canada.

Bryan lives in Caldwell, Idaho with his wife, Katie, and their two children, Lucy and Matthew. He recently lost his beloved corgi, Stoli while writing this book.

Michael Kroth

Michael Kroth is a professor of education in the Adult, Organizational Learning and Leadership program at the University of Idaho in Boise. He has written or coauthored six books, including *Transforming Work: The Five Keys to Achieving Trust, Commitment, and Passion in the Workplace* (2001); *The Manager as Motivator* (2006); *Career Development Basics* (2009); *Managing the Mobile Workforce: Leading, Building, and Sustaining Virtual Teams* (2010); and *Stories of Transformative Learning* (2014). His latest book is *Profound Living: Essays, Images, and Poetry* (2019).

Michael curates and writes for *Profound Living with Michael Kroth* (www.profoundliving.live), an online site with essays, photos, and poetry dedicated to contemplating what it means to have a profound life.

He is a lifelong and practicing Methodist who has developed a deep love of Catholicism through Catholic friends and mentors like Bryan Taylor and via opportunities for retreat at places like Mount Angel Abbey in Oregon; and the Marymount Hermitage, the Monastery of the Ascension, and the Nazareth Retreat Center (now closed), both located in Idaho. He has a wide-ranging interest in learning about all faith traditions and spirituality.

Michael has been married for 44 years to his wife, Lana. Piper and Shane are their cherished children. Grayson (Piper's son) and Alex and Madison (the children of Shane and his wife, Lisa) are their dearly loved grandchildren. Tinkerbell and Shelby, two precious rescue pups turned family members, round out Michael and Lana's household in Boise, Idaho.

Made in the USA
Las Vegas, NV
05 January 2022

40448950R00089